@therawcure

ɘƆA9Ƨ WA3ЯT ɘʜɈ

Gaia Speaks

Lessons Of Leadership, Love & Transformation

Written By: Jesse J. Jacoby

SoulSpire Publishing

Jacoby

SoulSpire Publishing
Guerneville, CA

ISBN: 978-0-9885920-8-7
Library of Congress Control Number: 2019911162

Cover art by: Gabriela Mejia @one_gemart
Cover design, font, and layout by: Qi Das @dreamcatchrqi
                        Hannah Harris @tropicannahh

Disclaimer

The teachings in this book are guidelines for healing humanity from the many vices that suppress truth and impair health. Although supported by nature, professional research, and scientific studies, some of the recommendations and suggestions may not be widely accepted in Western culture or the current paradigm that governs the economy.

Before making any decisions regarding prescription drug use, or procedures that could impact your health in any way, please consult with a naturopathic doctor or holistic health professional. The author is not liable for any verdicts, or their consequences, influenced from the lessons within.

When we lead with our heart and stand for what we know is right, the Universe works in our favor. Once we attune our frequency to harmonize with Earth we can find our center.

Dedication

These woven words of compassion, peace and wisdom are anointed with inviolable gratitude for the children of Earth and next seven generations. To Arlo, Alaeika, Calia, Krishna, Nevaeh, Zion and the many tribes of beautiful kids around the world who depend on clean air, intact forests, arable soil and pure water. The youth of today and tomorrow adapt to the culture they are immersed in, extract our values, and inherit this land. May they always be blessed with purity, enshrined in divine protection, and receive guidance and knowledge from wise teachers.

The origin of messages that compose this book were garnered from the wisdom of my Choctaw ancestors – Pushmataha and Moshulatubbee. The lessons enshrined in this publication are in honor of my native roots – my father, my grandmother, her mother, and all of her grandmother's who preceded her. For my mother, the mothers of my two children, and all other mothers.

These writings are reflections of the effusion of love we are gifted with every day from the unifying force of the *International Council of Thirteen Indigenous Grandmothers*. May their prayers continue to absolve us from struggle, satiate our hunger with nourishment, pacify us with security, fill our voids, and shower us with warmth. May their influence grow as they spread light to every region of this world with their sacred wisdom and Earth-based healing traditions.

"When the Grandmothers come from the four directions and speak, the world will heal." – Hopi Prophecy

Gaia Speaks is dedicated to organizations working to create new paradigms, and activists who risk their lives daily promoting compassion, equality and peace. A percentage of proceeds from all book sales will be divided in sixths and contributed to Earth Guardians (earthguardians.org), Sea Shepherd Conservation Society (*seashepherd.org*), International Anti-Poaching Foundation (*iapf.org*), Rainforest Alliance (rainforest-alliance.*org*), Leonardo DiCaprio Foundation (*leonardodicaprio.org*), and Center for Biological Diversity (*biologicaldiversity.org*).

Table of Contents

Author's Preface – My Transformation

I was raised in a suburb near the city of Chicago. Throughout my childhood I was subjected to a *police state*, engulfed in a web of lies that formulated my basic education, and estranged from my ancestral roots. My awareness was painted over by an inherited belief system that encouraged me to fit in to a misguided system not affiliated with my inherent virtues or intrinsic nature. The consciousness I was gifted with as part of my creation had been swindled by teachings that malign dignity and grace. I was a product of cultural conditioning and had earned my position as a victim of society.

I recall being manipulated into believing I needed to drink cow's milk to strengthen my bones, and that eggs and meat were needed in my diet for the protein required to sustain life. I trusted the food being served to me was empowering me when in actuality most of what I was fed was poisoning me. I was eating for calories and macronutrients, and neglecting the health of my organs, while omitting foods abundant with the most vital nutrients – being raw fruits and vegetables.

The public school curriculum taught me to honor and respect brutal conquerors of the past, despite their contributions to genocide. We learned extinction was somehow natural and that pollution was part of life. Textbooks proposed that habitat loss was the driving force behind extinction of species and extermination of cultures. They failed to explain how corporations and greed were responsible for the habitat loss killing off beautiful animals and decimating forests. When there was mention of saving rainforests, I never knew there were tribes of humans also living in these forests being massacred and threatened with extinction. As kids we are only taught what they want us to see. There were no classes offered instructing me how to grow my own food, regenerate land, meditate or practice mindfulness. Our inspiration was driven by a need to earn money, and we were urged to choose a career path that would define who we are and what we do.

I adapted through my upbringing to this culture of alcoholism, consumerism, degeneration, fast food and sports. While raised in a loving family and provided the necessities for survival, I knew something was missing. I could not allow myself to be conformed by this system and I lost interest in school. I was never sold on tradition or religion. Somewhere inside me I was aching for more, yet I was unsure what this substance was I sought after. I played sports, yet failed to pick up an instrument. I tried supplements and vitamins, but also experimented with alcohol and drugs. I started eating organic, yet still ingested foods not beneficial for my health. Eventually my distaste for the paradigm I was engulfed in landed me in juvenile Department of Corrections. I can relate with prisoners and caged farm animals.

I was taken from my home at fourteen and incarcerated for actions proportioned with a disconnect from my ancestors, and lack of a meaningful culture. In this refined version of America, I could not find a sense of purpose. Going to school, or working every day, was not fulfilling me. Spending weekends at parties where I poison myself deliberately with alcohol and drugs was only worsening my discontent. The only time I could ever find peace within was during adventures in nature. The problem I had was there is little nature still remaining in the Midwest region. Much of the land has been exploited for agriculture, commercial interests, housing, recreational uses and urban development. The only escape we have from this engineered life path are few small nature preserves that require transportation to visit.

This lack of nature nurtures boredom, and this leads us to search for interaction. Most people fill this void with alcohol, drugs and partying. We supplant emptiness with enormous amounts of unhealthful foods. We celebrate tradition by drinking alcohol and centering meals around dead animals. Night life equates to bar life. Energy is expended competing in sports rather than hiking through forests or harvesting food. We are told what to eat and what to wear through advertisements. We are indoctrinated to be helpless.

At sixteen I was again removed from my home and placed in a youth home for six months. Here I began noticing I had more to offer the world. The seventy other kids court-ordered to be in this program were all affiliated with gangs. They could not read and suffered from serious behavioral and learning disorders. I brought some books with me, one being Nelson Mandela's autobiography, *Long Walk To Freedom*. The man running the operation noticed my books and took interest in me. He promoted me to house coordinator, which was identical to being CEO of a company. I was responsible for managing my peers and assuring they each performed their daily job functions. Part of my duty was also to be of peer support to them whenever they needed to talk. The stories I heard from these other kids enlightened me and helped me to gain compassion. I quickly learned that these children were lacking love and nourishment. Simply because they were immersed in gang life and destructive with their lifestyle, this did not mean they were not humans capable of adapting change. These kids were experiencing what any other child would being raised in an environment surrounded by drugs, gangs and hostility. Their only sources of nourishment come from convenience stores. Liquor stores are on every corner. Children mimic what they see, and when you put them in a position where all they witness is poison to their consciousness, they inevitably become misguided.

When I was released from the Gateway program I had acquired wisdom that motivated me to go back to school and accomplish what is expected of me. I realized if I did the bare minimum and applied myself in class, then I could do what I wanted once we were released. I turned my life around and graduated from high school on high honor roll. For my academic achievement and community involvement I was rewarded with a scholarship for full tuition to attend college. I spent five years total in college studying business administration, exercise science and kinesiology. I relocated to Boca Raton, FL, and completed my internship at the *Institute of Human Performance*. I started my career in fitness.

I enjoyed my job as a performance coach and personal trainer. My life path was devoted to service, giving back, and helping others understand the importance of health and wellness. While this work fulfilled me in many ways, I still felt I was missing something. For much of my adolescence I had watched my brother suffer from the symptoms of psychotropic drug poisoning. From the age of thirteen until he was twenty-two he was experimented on by psychiatrists and doctors. They were force-feeding him lithium and pills, and subduing him with psycho-shock therapy. He was conned into thinking he needed these pills, and they trapped him in a system that circulates around crimes against humanity. I watched his mental health gradually decline each year until he was a fraction of the beautiful human he was before the systematic poisoning. At twenty-two he decided he had enough and walked face-first into an oncoming passenger train. His suicide triggered me to find natural ways to heal and treat depression.

My search for natural remedies helped me discover plant-based nutrition. I soon realized nutrition was my real passion. I published my first book, *The Raw Cure: Healing Beyond Medicine*, at twenty-six and moved to California to work for a vegan culinary school. I had never been to this region of the country, but I had an urge within insisting that I explore the area. In California is where I met my first redwood tree. This meeting aroused a newfound peace within, broadened my imagination, and revived my creativity.

The nature I was surrounded by in Mendocino County filled me with a satiety I had never before experienced. I remember hugging these trees and praying with them. I thought of my brother and how much this experience would have uplifted him. For the first time in my life I experienced complete contentment. I did not need social interaction if I had mountains, rivers, tall trees, and wild animals to observe. I recognized how vital of a role nature plays in acquiring peace of mind. The anxiety, bipolar, and depressive disorders that plague most of Western society can be attributed to a disconnect from nature.

Being immersed in this enchanting environment, coupled with eating a vibrant plant-based diet, elevated me higher than ever before. I finally experienced the depth of spirituality. While I have always prayed to a higher power, or Great Spirit, I never fully understood who or what these prayers were being directed toward. I only embraced the idea that praying felt good and brought me clarity and hope. Sometimes I would pray simply as routine. Being surrounded by nature in California, I had extracted a spiritual energy in the redwood forests that guided my newfound life path. I would elicit fresh ideas and siphon messages from the natural habitat. After long days in the woods, I dedicated hours of my time to writing, and attaching understanding to the lessons and teachings from the forest. I started closing my prayers with Aho opposed to Amen. This is a prayerful Native American expression. The redwoods directed me to reconnect with my Choctaw heritage and learn more about my ancestors. I started praying to inherit their wisdom and found myself drawn back to a culture uninfluenced by Western society.

This love culture I began manifesting and calling in magnetized me to other people walking an identical path. I was introduced to native plant medicines from Central and South America. When used ceremonially, these medicines bring us awareness, clarity, knowledge and wisdom. Plant medicine ceremonies introduce us to true culture, give us a chance to speak our truth, and help us establish identity. I picked up the guitar and started writing songs and making music. I became more conscientious of how much my freedom is associated with my buying power. What I contribute toward with my dollar also supports my well-being. My lifestyle in no way harms the livelihood of other species. I live as a purist – someone who refuses to allow impurities to enter my terrain.

This book is a compilation of teachings, useful knowledge, and writings Mother Earth is urging me to share to elevate consciousness, eradicate extinction, raise awareness, and save the planet from further destruction. Thank you for taking this journey with me.

Filling The Void

There is a soul resting inside of this beautiful instrument embodying my being.

Her essence captivates light.
His presence beams through my pores.

My skin is glowing like fireflies emanating life force.
Uniting masculine warmth and feminine strength.

The love flowing through this body, spirit and mind is a psychoactive expansion of consciousness, altering fantasy into reality.

Fairy tales are transmuted into forest trails. I walk this path of surrender to where my heart feels centered.

Guiding forces lead me to enchanting places beyond the world of make believe I grew up being pressured into accepting as my only option.

Now I summon the change we all are seeking.

I am peeking in divine regions of an imagination that refuses to sleep through extinction of languages and cultures.

I chase a mirage of ethnic diversity, coexisting with freedom, in a world without this disease called separation that shatters any chances of attaining world peace.

Wars sabotage the livelihood of planet Earth.
Court systems batter individual paths to grace.
Poverty cripples aspirations of Third World heroes.
Pollution poisons indigenous rivers.
This demolition of goodness does not slow.

The real battle I aim to conquer begins within my own temple.

My quest is to find glory without materialism or power, through meditation and meteor showers of self-satisfaction.

I accept my worth, and embrace my position as a soldier of consciousness.

I am blessed with wings that help me soar above the storms watering ambitions down.

My claws pierce the chains that anchor so many into shallow grounds, freeing me to ascend higher into sacred spaces all around.

My bark has been burned and scarred and beneath the char this soul of mine is still unharmed.

Stab wounds from other spirits waiting to be found could not break apart my white wolf heart.

Pain befriended my never ending mending from being misunderstood by those pretending to be affectionate, yet still afraid to embrace the role of authentic.

My soul and I.

We resurrect from emptiness, filled with light.
Sirius shines through us with radiance, piercing into night.

We refuse to be buried beneath weaknesses ashes.
Honoring the connection between our roots and branches.
Protecting the core that holds us together, the same way love prevents the world from ending.

Eternal liberation is my right.
I will not lose this fight.
I am empowered by every experience in life.

Awareness is an eternal blessing.
I travel to the fifth dimension where spiritual wisdom prevails.

I am enabled to unearth my roots so I can exhume the artifacts needed for all people to unite in accord. I find the disarmament of greed is the sharpest sword, and dissolvement of control is the only gun that will overpower our lust for gold.

Paper money always results in poor people's food being rationed.

Currency is an illness and the cure is talent and sharing passion.

Mainstream kills and ties the neck of innocence in a noose.
There is no way to trust a truce with ignorance.
When education is manufactured from arrogance, all we learn is doom.

My soul is aching for what the schools cannot teach, and what no reverend has the wits to preach.

I am pursuing what preserves my ability to love so I will never be tempted by propaganda, hatred, cultural conditioning, envy, guns or drugs.

I am on the prowl to get up in every orifice of tenderness and launch an Apocalypse to eradicate anger, expel confusion, and exterminate racism.

Command and conquer has drilled so many holes we are now burying our survival into an emptiness that is the only lasting attachment after profits vanish.

How do we fill voids of abandonment, abuse, betrayal and neglect without laughter, happiness, true love, real friends and unbroken families?

My mission is to revive the music that has been silenced by generations of armies programmed to lose.

My soul exists to prove competition is a tragedy, we all have the capacity to free ourselves from material fantasies, and love is the predominant entity that will rescue this galaxy.

Introduction

The global ethnosphere is governed by a universal language – the foundation which is centered around biodiversity, coexistence, compassion, generosity, health, love and multicultural vastness. Beyond this supreme voice are extensions of diversified communication channels. To adapt and integrate into the body of multiple languages requires a relentless pursuit for understanding. When we neglect the primitive discourse naturally ingrained in our conscience, all other communication outlets are fragmented.

What we are witnessing today is Civilization adapting to speaking a dialect that revolves around anger, arrogance, confusion, depression, greed, ignorance, misunderstanding, poor health, and racism. A quest for one single education system, coupled with the universal acceptance of a sole language – being English – drives the agenda which is destroying mankind and this beautiful planet we depend on for survival.

Human greed has always been insatiable. This is a demon who haunts us all, and many of us are programmed to consistently lose to the demands of this force. Millions of dollars are being invested into dams, mining machines, oil refineries, logging trucks, and destruction equipment while attention is diverted away from the profitable agendas that kill countless thousands of people and other species each day.

Pollution is at intolerable levels. Much of this arises from animal exploitation. The incompetence of a culture lacking the atoms of goodness that are authentic and not generic, and which are needed for real change to occur. Animal agriculture is not a way of life, so culture should never be embodied into the word used to describe the senseless, atrocious practice of raising animals to die. Without meat, dairy, and eggs we would erase all disease and the end of violence and wars would soon be inevitable.

Jacoby

A nuisance that often goes unnoticed is our misdirected appetite. A disconnect of the mind and heart. When we ingest health-depleting particles that are formed, shaped, and marketed as food we begin harboring an imbalance of gut bacteria. In order to metabolize whatever these particles are, we generate more of a certain microbe or bacterial strain, creating clusters of harmful organisms within. These microbes are conscious beings who are capable of intercepting nerve signals and communicating with our brain. When this microbial consciousness gains too much control, the parasitic beings drive us to eat food laced with drugs. If we feed the unnatural urges, symptoms can be reflective of anger and ugliness. These microbes in the gut are master manipulators and are on a mission to takeover and destroy the organism which they occupy. Sadly, they do not stop with plotting to destroy us, they also want to destruct this planet.

Human ignorance is becoming unstoppable and the arrogance is plausible. The power hungry are dying from a disease called insatiety. They have every material desire, but cannot find what satisfies those with less until they understand these substances could never be mined. All people who believe killing animals is okay and who support the logging of trees, fishing of oceans, chemical poisoning of all soil and water sources, damning of rivers, fracking for gas, drilling for oil, mining of all precious solids and medicating of the human population have been infected with a virus that cannot be cured with material items. In fact, materialism only feeds this viral demon. In Ojibwa culture, this virus of the mind is known as windigo – a destructive spirit driven by excess, greed and selfish consumption. To expel this violent force, we are required to adapt a healthier lifestyle and find connection with the soul of nature.

The book, Gaia Speaks, is based on a series of lessons which I perceive as downloads I have received from the Spirit of Gaia – or who some refer to as Pachamama. She is the mother, or grandmother of nature, and guardian of the beauty which remains on this planet we all occupy. In some northern Native American cultures, she is known as Maka Ina.

I am able to receive these messages by partaking in meditations where I release my consciousness to nature. As I surrender, I take on the ethos of the ocean, rivers, trees and wind. I often experience these reflections near the cliff's edge on the northwest pacific coast, or deep in the redwood forests. As I rest on the windy coastline, I let go of all I know, and allow the wind and ocean to bless me with new thoughts and ideas. While in the woods, as I rest up against the beautiful body of a redwood giant, I let go of all I am bound to and learn from the trees lessons of resiliency, strength and wisdom. I am able to discern between what matters and what is obsolete.

If we put the dollar aside, we can easily strategize ways to heal our wounds without contributing to the core of what is rooted in all ills. The only pill we need is nature in harmony. What does not enrich all of this biosphere is only harming us. All of the starving children, their hunger is cancerous to you and me. As more species vanish, we lose future human generations. Every dollar we spend makes an impact. Each meal we eat leaves an imprint on some region of the world. We can continue buying what imprisons us in gloom and sickness, or we can mindfully purchase what resurrects health and happiness. Astute mindfulness and elevated consciousness are elixirs needed as step one for the reversal process.

Gaia instructs us to let go of six of mankind's reckless actions to solidify a harmonious and peaceful manifesto for coexisting with preservation and love as foundational values. Our mission is to eradicate animal agriculture (feedlots and factory farms); end deforestation; stop the slaughter of marine life; discontinue drilling and fracking for oil and gas; remove the dams which block the river's flow; and banish all harmful chemicals. As these actions cease, peace surmounts.

I write these words manifesting change. This book serves as a platform for resurrecting the power and strength of humanity, unifying with the guiding forces who aim to resolve conflict, and cleaning up the polluted mess known as Western culture.

Spiritual Aid

Free souls of wise teachers bless the minds of those who are open with ancient knowledge. They visit us in our sleep, while we pray in the sun on the beach, and when we wrap our arms around trees. When we call they appear. They are ancestral guides, angelic beings, archangels, deities, spiritual entities and tribal chiefs. They feed us clues to mine sacred wisdom from long lost tombs. Our role is to spread this information to the masses, redirect the troops, and dismantle the powers that suppress us.

They tell us climate change is real. They show us in the thousands of species that are vanishing still. They speak for African lions, elephants and rhinos. They weep for sea turtles on Galapagos. They cry gray whale tears and grieve for dolphins. They are drawn to compassion. They seek warriors who are courageous and determined. They provide guidance for activists.

These spirit guides appreciate intelligence. They nurture with hope those of us who fight to uncover truth. They bless us with strength of voice and encourage us to emerge as the leaders we are. They honor how we treat this ecosystem as our home and reward us for conservation.

Our spiritual professors are loyal like wolves. They exhibit the warmth of polar bears and enshrine those they find in divine protection. These teachers urge us to contribute to the regeneration of Earth. They only ask of us to find empowerment in everything, to never remain silent about atrocity, and to fight with our hearts and minds to take back the purity this Earth was built from. Only the people united can overpower the force that is reckoning this planet. When we are distanced from our connection with Earth, our intellect declines.

"As well as the carbon dioxide pollution of our physical environment, we can speak of the spiritual pollution of our human environment: the toxic and destructive atmosphere we are creating with our way of consuming. We need to consume in such a way that truly sustains our peace and happiness. Only when we are sustainable as humans will our civilization become sustainable. Happiness is possible in the here and now." – Thich Nhat Hanh

Man Diminishing – Decline of Intellect

When corrupted by artificial culture, people accommodate space for alcohol, chemicals, drugs, foods void of nourishment and pills. While able to survive and withstand these imbalances for a lengthy duration of time, they operate at a frequency below their potentiality. They are programmed to live unnaturally. This model of living can be compared to the life cycle of a genetically-modified plant. Crops that are genetically-engineered are overdosed with chemicals and pesticides, yet designed to withstand this assault and still produce yield. While the plant still grows and bears fruit, nutritional content is of lesser quality, and vitality is inferior to plants grown organically without chemical poisoning.

The aptitude and merit of man today is a fraction of what could be when nourished organically, living in compliance with human nature, and eating compatibly with the anatomy of the human body. The psyche of society has been weakened and reduced through docility, and submission to inherited dietary patterns and lifestyle acquisitions. Congruent with what governs the economy during adolescence, each generation is raised in a different bubble of absurdity. This can be identified as *generational degeneration*. When we are indoctrinated with inept information presented as knowledge, and habituated to adapt unhealthful routines during childhood, our status declines. Intelligence is reduced and moral values decrease. Strength atrophies and wisdom is obscured.

We seem to be aloof to the magnitude of how our negligence imperils the planet. As substandard ideals are normalized, we are conditioned to contribute to unnecessary planetary degradation as we consume our way through life. Simply being raised in a Western society requires that we inadvertently support animal agriculture, chemical production and application, deforestation, drilling, fracking and mining. Until new paradigms are constructed, there is great difficulty attached to freeing ourselves from this propagandism.

Similar to how humans farm cattle and livestock, people are also being cultivated to conform to preconditioned beliefs, customs, norms and traditions. We are instructed from childhood to eat in accordance with how likely industries are to profit from the foods we ingest. We learn to abandon history so we can regurgitate a carefully crafted timeline of events that are fabricated and untrue. The information we are force-fed through public education and mainstream news outlets fattens our minds with substance of low frequency that diminishes intellect and lowers IQ – akin to how livestock are fattened with health degrading feed solely to generate more meat for agribusinesses to rake in higher profit margins.

As we acculturate to this flagrant life path, we become expendable. From the perspective of those who operate these human farms, all citizens of society are as relevant as their social security number in regard to their worth. Identical to how cows are branded and tagged with symbols, prisoners are identified by number. If we choose not to conform to the molding of social order, prison is often where we are placed.

When we are not collectively working toward improving our living conditions and bettering the planet, we function for causes that worsen our circumstances. Billions of humans who easily plunge into a system of deceit are considered as commodities to those who live and operate outside of this paradigm. From their perspective we are invasive and must be exterminated.

"Many of us think we need more money, more power or more status before we can be happy. We are so busy spending our lives chasing after money, power and status that we ignore all the conditions for happiness already available. At the same time, we lose ourselves in buying and consuming things we do not need, putting a heavy strain on both our body and the planet. Yet much of what we drink, eat, watch, read or listen to is toxic – polluting our body and mind with violence, anger, fear and despair." – Thich Nhat Hanh

Verdict On Overpopulation

Two proposals inscribed in the Georgia Guidestones are to *keep the population of humanity at or below five-hundred million*, and *guide reproduction wisely*. With the estimated population surpassing seven billion, those with control are using extermination methods to reduce this number. These methods of depopulation include inducing infertility, spreading disease, creating wars, and mass widespread poisoning of air, food, people, soil and water.

Agenda 21 is an action plan of the United Nations to downsize the world population by a large percentage before the year 2030. To carry out this mission they are adding fluoride to municipal water sources, spraying crops with pesticides such as glyphosate and various phosphates, adding chemicals and endocrine disruptors to foods, spraying metal oxides into the atmosphere, prescribing harmful medications that prolong sickness, and misinforming the public about the efficacy and safety of vaccines while mass-inoculating millions of innocent children with gene-altering cocktails in syringes.

When the population is crippled, ill and rapidly dying from chronic disease and sickness, this further depletes the planet. There are better means for managing population growth. Rather than poisoning, we can promote health, encourage cleanliness, and redistribute and regenerate land.

Humans are mass-breeding farm animals, and mass-producing harmful chemicals. For every person alive there are ten farm animals. These chickens, cows, pigs, sheep and other farmed animals are responsible for emitting far more greenhouse gases, expending vaster amounts of resources, and occupying larger areas of land than humans and all other species combined. There are close to seventy billion farm animals competing with seven billion humans – and the remaining wild animals – for food, land and water. To effectively combat population growth, humanity needs to formulate a new education system, and promote teachings that are useful for improving conditions of life on Earth.

Education Renovation

Intrinsically, the nature of man is non-conformist. While the idea of a universal education system has potential to be effective globally, the confusion circulating around the agenda of the pseudo-leadership clan has tainted many opportunities to share useful information and disseminate widespread knowledge. Delusional men who bludgeon the righteousness of mankind blemish the principles of goodness by clustering together teachings comprised of nonsense to mold and format artificial life paths constructed to increase corporate and industry profits.

Children are programmed to be indoctrinated with information that has been strategically formulated into a curriculum, and has no useful rhetoric or underlying values. The result, inevitably, is dysfunction. Children today are victims of the insatiable demands of those who destroy for profit and thrive on the enslavement of others.

Education fails us by refusing to implement and honor the wisdom and teachings of other cultures who express their language in fashions more meaningfully and less ruinous. The sacredness of nature is painted over as an economic benefactor. Chemicals are viewed as opportunities for stock values to rise. Water is dictated as a commodity and declared as property. Animals are farmed as objects and ruthlessly slaughtered to be manufactured into health-depleting foods. Agriculture has been directed away from regenerating land to being a major contributor to desertification.

Men who cannot abdicate their stance or position on something solely to protect profits, at the expense of the greater good of the planet, are criminals. Their crime is treason to Gaia – the only noble entity we are ever to pledge our allegiance to. When a man is categorized as being powerful because of a title or position ruling as such, and he abuses this role, he is guilty of treason to the children and people who have been forced to comply with his corruption. His army – a branch of law enforcement – blindly terrorizes innocent people who refuse to be conformed into a counterfeit way of life.

Among the many problems attached to the public school system today is that the teachings are comprised of elementary subjects that do not align with what is needed universally for harmony and peace to be established. In a sense, anxiety can be analogous to society hiding behind the lies plastered over all truths by this hierarchy. The neurodevelopmental irregularities acquired by kids stems from degradation of learning. Subjugating of the human mind through erroneous studies and paltry content pollutes culture, enables further obliteration of our landbase, and warps the nature of man.

Man was created to coexist, find equanimity, and work together to gather ways to better and improve the planet. No other being can extract energy from nature like man. Similarly, man is capable of manipulating other entities to benefit his demands and desires. When energy is extracted from nature solely to destroy nature this leads to a planet in peril. The actions of mankind today are not advantageous, beneficial or regenerative to any species – plant or mammal.

We are witnessing the extraction of energy from coal, oil, water and wind to generate power for machinery to butcher forests, harm animals, poison each other, and empower technology. The costs of this intrusion are criminality, disease, enslavement, extinction of species, famine, genocide, pollution, poverty, wars and water scarcity. Humans manipulate animals to work for them and enslave them to help carry out their agenda to control, destroy and imprison. We see this with horses being used for horsepower, dogs trained for hunting and assisting law enforcement, mice and monkeys used for experimentation in vivisection labs, exotic creatures locked in zoos for entertainment, and farm animals exploited for fur, meat and milk.

If we applied the same energy that is being expended to extract and manipulate energy from nature and other entities toward healing and conserving the planet, we would witness true progress. The opposite of progress today is congress. The Government system that has been implanted into the structure of society alludes to evil. The format of life through the universal education system paves a path for disease and suffering. Much of what we are fed as knowledge is not congruent with the wisdom and teachings our spirits desire. This is reflected in the collapse of culture, absence of leadership, alarming rates of depression and suicide, unacceptable prison population, and ceaselessness of war.

We could never advance as a civilization, society, or species when we are punished since birth with poisons in the form of animal-based foods, electromagnetic radiation frequencies, food chemicals, fluoridated water, pesticides, pharmaceutical pills, sulfur aerosols, technological intrusion and vaccines. These obstructions are utilized to conform and break the human spirit. This formatting of the nature of man is crafted generationally and woven into the psyche of the parent who is expected to adhere to certain customs and norms as they raise children. Kids are immersed into an ocean of misunderstanding and they inherit the same intellectual incongruities as their predecessors. The soul of nature is depleted parallel to the spirit of man being plagiarized by a systematic web of confusion that has been compiled as standard universal education.

This chemical poisoning of the planet equates to the conformity of mankind and the stronghold over the mind of man. The weak and puny orchestrators of these injustices hide behind material objects that temporarily fill permanent voids. They extract energy from programmed people who join militias of armed men, fool them into believing they are fighting for freedom, and use this collective force to impede on the primitive nature and values of man. As armies and troops they travel the world to disrupt harmony, terrorize families, massacre tribes of indigenous people, install elementary government regimes that enforce laws protecting corporations, push the universal education system, extract resources from land, pollute soil and water with chemicals and farm animal manure, and poison all life.

We are raised to believe Patriotism stands for bullying other nations and binding ourselves to values incompatible with the goodness that is our birthright. If we love the country where we reside, then we must do all we can to protect this land from poison and pollution. Politicians provide concierge services to those responsible for degrading the land we love.

The command and conquer mentality has swept through nearly every nation – ruthlessly and dishonorably. Profits are generated from the conquering of tribes, and obliteration of innocence. Those who are composing this insurgence outwit by being manipulative – not potent or influential. They extract control and power from energy that is intended for righteousness and wisdom. They pervert spirituality with religion and use missionaries to spread disease and poisons through the areas they occupy.

Spirituality is masked by sets of rules declared and proposed by those who demand merit and prestige. Their goal is to castigate the purity and innocence of the human mind that is unscathed by this pseudo-civilization acquired by Western regions. After their spirit is broken, children are stripped of mental clarity, physical immunity and emotional well-being. They are soon directed toward a practiced religion. Their goodness and dignity are pirated and embezzled by the system of lies that constitute what has reshaped culture.

A single solution is not enough. We need dualutions. To resolve the serious catastrophes we are witnessing, we start by introducing regenerative agriculture, water-fueled vehicles, hemp and bamboo farming, and a complete restructuring of the fallacy known as healthcare. In addition, we ban deforestation, eliminate pesticides and phase out animal agriculture. Schools must begin to teach children to be healthy, and medical organizations can no longer hijack the health of kids with pills and shots.

Without a close relationship to nature, and a rekindling of our companionship with Gaia, mankind will continue to be depleted and pushed deeper into despair. We need effective, uncensored leadership.

Emergence of Leaders

To decode what qualities must be exuded to emerge as an incorruptible leader requires a lifetime of noncompliance, perseverance, recusancy and resiliency. Leaders must honor truth over bribery and manipulation. Simply gaining notoriety as a leader in the current paradigm is not satisfying when we know that imports, exports, rising stock numbers and a booming economy does nothing to fix the broken system which disassembles cultures and governs our way of life. Our heart and soul both tell us that we must encourage others to stop contributing to what dismantles harmony if we wish to accrue lasting and widespread global change.

The extirpation of other nations to sustain economic growth in the country where our ancestors once lived wholesomely, without prejudice or hatred, does not align with meaningful core values. We cannot accept this paradigm. We are capable of coexisting with nature, the animal Kingdom, and all life without needing to control, imprison, penetrate, poison and pollute. America is not defined by the reckless adaptations acquired through the indoctrination of idiocy. The inexplicable beauty of this nation permeates from our relationship with peace. To divorce ourselves from this compatibility is to succumb to harsh circumstances.

In February 2019, an American politician claimed that the real national emergency this country is facing is that people are *dying from lack of healthcare.* She expressed this statement on a social media platform and millions of people agreed with her. To clarify, people are not dying from a lack of healthcare. This business claiming to provide healthcare never offers or promotes cures, they only complicate the processes in the body further and greatly exacerbate disease symptoms. The national emergency America is facing is a lack of clean food and water, chemical pollution, and a toxic culture. A large majority of food sources in packages are saturated with food chemicals and drugs. The municipal water is contaminated with chlorine, fluoride, glyphosate, prescription drug residues and several other harmful compounds. When consumers develop illness from the poisoned water and food, they receive *healthcare* in the form of more drugs that are toxic to the body. This system annihilates health. People are literally dying from healthcare.

What America lacks is a presence of real leaders. The men and women in congress who have been enacted as leaders do nothing to help people. They are bought and paid for by corporations who want to sell chemicals and drugs, drill and frack for oil and gas, cut down trees, and poison all water sources. The notion of relying on anyone outside of within our own being to improve our quality of life, or enrich the reality of our limited perception, is the epitome of a system that is not working. An elected candidate is only amassing change for himself – which he is responsible for – to protect his way of life. We do not benefit from either side.

The herds of a brainwashed culture displaying a lack of understanding by enrolling into divided political systems that disassemble unification are stepping out of their power by waiting on other people to somehow liberate them from their limiting beliefs. The propaganda manipulating us into believing our vote matters is stealing our democracy.

In the political system two candidates are chosen as leaders. These two are often ecocidal criminals selected by wealthy people who govern the corporations that rule the economy. If either candidate was an effective leader they would be chosen by the people and would refuse to accept money from corporations seeking to fulfill their agendas. Leaders do not steal from the poor. Leaders do not give executive orders to kill. Leaders do not support corporations that poison the planet. Leaders do not have agendas overseas to invade and conquer for resources they do not need. Where are the leaders promoting world peace, unity and kindness? They do exist.

"We have the money, power, medical understanding, scientific know-how, love, and community to produce a kind of human paradise, but we are led by the least among us – the least intelligent and least visionary." – Terrence McKenna

If we collectively desire the creation of jobs there are an array of wonderful opportunities available. Rather than resurrecting employment in an industry dependent on non-renewable resources – such as building dams, coal mines, developing infrastructure, fracking, logging, and drilling for oil – we can build a new paradigm.

There are new industries emerging from clean energy sources; alternative medicines; remediation of the forests, land, and soil; and sustainable agricultural practices. By investing in jobs that require the farming of bamboo, hemp, and other industrial fibers we can save what remains of the forests. By legalizing marijuana, millions of jobs will open up in the growing cannabis industry – which is arguably the most powerful medicine for treating a multitude of health ailments.

By phasing out dirty energy sources like coal and oil we can generate millions of opportunities for employment installing solar panels and building electric cars here in America. Abolishing the biotech industry, banning genetically modified seeds and chemicals, and encouraging the transition to universal veganism will open doors for jobs that require the remediation of land and forests, and growing an abundance of fruits, grains and vegetables to replace feedlots. Instead of constructing new dams that stagnate our rivers, we can hire people to start removing the dams already in place as solar power makes hydro power obsolete. This is how we will make America great. The butterfly effect will have a global impact.

In America we are taught that terror organizations operate everywhere outside of where we reside. The truth is that the regime governing this country aggregates more terror around the world than anywhere else. In fact, all terrorist agendas in other nations are rooted in the pursuit of economic growth in the richest nations. The terrorism ploy is only a mask to divert angst and hatred toward outside forces that do not exist. We create wars where resources are most abundant, install government regimes in those locations, accuse them of fictitious crimes, supply them with weapons, and start wars that defy nature.

America was built on genocide, but we can clear the energetic karma by remediating the land, cleaning up the atrocities, and using our power and prestige to promote peace globally. The discovery of America by tyrants and murderers escalated into a hostile takeover. Indigenous clans who occupied this land were slaughtered and subdued to mass-extermination and crimes against humanity. Among those who were forced to surrender to the savageness of these foreign intruders was Chief Seattle. He wrote with passion in an attempt to save the land he loved so much. His letter explains in depth how the views of my ancestors were congruent with coexistence, harmony and peace. He stated, *"The President in Washington sends word that he wishes to buy our land. But how can you buy or sell the sky? The land? The idea is strange to us. If we do not own the freshness of the air and the sparkle of the water, how can you buy them?*

Every part of the earth is sacred to my people. Every shining pine needle, every sandy shore, every mist in the dark woods, every meadow, every humming insect. All are holy in the memory and experience of my people. We know the sap which courses through the trees as we know the blood that courses through our veins. We are part of the earth as Earth is part of us. The perfumed flowers are our sisters. The bear, the deer, the great eagle – these are our brothers. The rocky crests, the dew in the meadow, the body heat of the pony, and man all belong to the same family.

The shining water that moves in the streams and rivers is not just water, but the blood of our ancestors. If we sell you our land, you must remember that the land we sell still holds her sacredness. Each glossy reflection in the clear waters of the lakes tells of events and memories in the life of my people. The water's murmur is the voice of my father's father. The rivers are our brothers. They quench our thirst. They carry our canoes and feed our children. So you must give the rivers the kindness that you would give any brother.

Jacoby

If we sell you our land, remember that the air is precious to us, that the air shares her spirit with all the life that she supports. The wind that gave our grandfather his first breath also received his last sigh. The wind also gives our children the spirit of life. So if we sell our land, you must maintain the sacredness, as a place where man can go to taste the wind that is sweetened by the meadow flowers.

Will you teach your children what we have taught our children? That the earth is our mother? What befalls the earth befalls all the sons of the earth. This we know: the earth does not belong to man, man belongs to the earth. All things are connected like the blood that unites us all. Man did not weave the web of life, he is merely a strand in the web. Whatever he does to the web, he does to himself. One thing we know: our God is also your God. The earth is precious to him and to harm the earth is to heap contempt on our creator.

Your destiny is a mystery to us. What will happen when the buffalo are all slaughtered? The wild horses tamed? What will happen when the secret corners of the forest are heavy with the scent of many men and the view of the ripe hills is blotted with talking wires? Where will the thicket be? Gone! Where will the eagle be? Gone! And what is to say goodbye to the swift pony and then hunt? The end of living and the beginning of survival.

When the last red man has vanished with this wilderness, and his memory is only the shadow of a cloud moving across the prairie, will these shores and forests still be here? Will there be any of the spirit of my people left?

We love this earth as a newborn loves his mother's heartbeat. So, if we sell you our land, love this land as we have loved her. Care for this land, as we have cared for her. Hold in your mind the memory of the land as she rests when you receive her. Preserve the land for all children, and love this land, as God loves us. As we are part of the land, you too are part of the land. This earth is precious to us. The planet is also precious to you.

One thing we know – there is only one God. No man, be he Red man or White man, can be apart. We are brothers after all".

How aligned are your values with those embraced by Chief Seattle? Are you giving kindness to the rivers? Do you recognize the sacredness in each pine needle? With each step you take are you massaging this planet with the soles of your feet or leaving an indentation of annihilation? Our insubordinate ways have dismantled the web of life Chief Seattle spoke of. We have failed to honor the life force of the land as our protector, only source of nourishment, and ultimately as our mother.

Much of the habitable land on this planet has been commandeered by corporations and is being depleted further daily. As more of nature is ruined, the health of humanity declines. To improve health and extend longevity we need to care for our planet. We begin by cleaning up our diet. We use the advantage of our purchasing power to resurrect beauty rather than contributing to decimation. We become the needed change.

Each of us carries within the capacity to effectively lead. We can be influential to our family members, friends, colleagues and all who we associate with. We start by customizing personal change. Once we adapt to a lifestyle that does not promote harm, we can define what we stand for. When we are aware of what drives and motivates us to better ourselves and those around us, our duty is to spread the knowledge and wealth.

We can no longer depend on others for happiness and well-being. The spark we need to build new paradigms, collapse unjust regimes, and revolutionize health is waiting to ignite in you. If you are growing weary of feeling stuck, sick, policed and hopeless, do your part to clean up the planet and stop contributing to her destruction. Gaia is waiting for you. Your health and well-being are interrelated with hers.

"Wakan Tanka, Great Mystery. Teach me how to trust the senses of my body and the blessings of my spirit. Connect my heart with my inner knowing, intuition, and mind. Teach me how to confide in these elements so I may enter my sacred space and love beyond all fears. Guide me to walk in balance with the passing of each glorious sun." – Lakota Prayer

Be Like A Tree

By observing trees in nature, we can more easily determine what we stand for as individuals. Trees withstand all weather conditions. They are able to survive the harshest winters, hottest summer days, most torrential storms, blazing fires and long droughts. From the seed to sapling stage, all the way until they emerge tall and strong, they serve a purpose. No matter what their circumstance, they keep standing. They know their role. The intrinsic nature of a tree is to give.

Trees can claim amphibians, animals, birds, humans, insects, microorganisms and plants as dependents. They provide shelter for living organisms and food for several more. Trees even work synergistically with fungal threads underground to transport nutrients to other plants and trees. Humans have devastatingly reached a level where we are now dependent on trees for what many of us think are necessities. Rather than cutting trees down for the resources they provide, we can enhance evolution by learning from these gentle beings.

We learn from trees about the strength of resiliency. We can identify what we stand for when comparing our lives to trees. To be like a tree we are required to embrace certain lifestyle characteristics. We recognize that we can also claim many living organisms as dependents. Animals and plants are stripped of life daily because of our careless decisions.

To stand like a tree requires that we are giving, and willing to offer a helping hand. If we are in a position where possible, we provide shelter for those in need. At times we take on harsh conditions and are required to overcome serious obstacles. We must be capable of adapting to any environment, and not only surviving, but also providing strength, nourishment and shelter.

Always stand for what you know in your heart is right. Uncover veils that hide faulty components of crumbling paradigms. Be a source of light. Spread your branches wide and far to accommodate all who lean on you for support, love and healing. Feed the starving souls who seek true knowledge with the most nourishing fruits, plants, seeds and wisdom.

Planetary Health Equates To Physical Well-Being

Anthropocentrism is the belief that wilderness is wasted unless developed. Human existence and human desires are perceived to be of central importance to the universe. Biocentrism is a knowingness that development destroys nature, thereby polluting our air, soil and water. Humans are not perceived to possess any right whatsoever to reduce the diversity and richness of life for any reason outside of vital needs for survival. A shift to biocentrism is imminent.

Gaia challenges us to start planting trees. Designate a space in your yard for a garden. Tend to plants and be a caretaker for nature. As you participate in this art of nurturing take note of what is happening within your body. Notice how your skin is getting softer. See the newfound beauty emerging from the glow that now emanates from your cheeks as you smile. Be mindful of how your health begins to improve as you supplement nature with your love. As a child blossoms, grows and matures into a beautiful man or woman when surrounded by affection, kindness and love, nature also blooms when doused with this goodness.

If you aspire to eliminate disease and sickness in the world, divert your energy away from the medical establishment and vaccine industry and get to the root of the problem. Our soil is sick, the forests are dying, water is poisoned and wild animals and crops are increasingly becoming more prone to disease. If we clean up our soil, nourish the land, purify water, tend to crops and animals, and remediate forests then we will discover the only way to eliminate disease and sickness.

There is an interrelation between our health and the health of our planet. Our mission is to honor this connection and help amass the needed change. We can reclaim our culture and implement all of the necessities for establishing harmony and peace into a diverse way of life.

"To touch the Earth is to have harmony with Nature." – Oglala Sioux

Love Culture

"We have to create culture. We can no longer watch television, read magazines, or listen to NPR. We must create our own roadshow. If you are worrying about pop musicians or political nonsense, then you are disempowered. You are giving away your livelihood to icons which are maintained by an electronic media. This propaganda drives you to want to dress like X or have lips like Y. This represents cultural diversion. What is important is you, your friends, and your associations. Your highs, your orgasms, your hopes, your plans, and your fears are real. When we are told that we are unimportant and peripheral, we lose our sense of wonder. When we are instructed to get a degree, job, or this and that, we become a player. This is not a game we want to play. Your best action is to reclaim your mind and get your reality out of the hands of the cultural engineers who want to turn you into a half-baked moron consuming all this trash that is being manufactured out of the bones of a dying world." – Terrence McKenna

America is severely lacking culture. We are raised in a society that manipulates primitive customs, ideals and traditions into profitable opportunities. Indigenous culture poses a serious threat to the establishment in developed nations because immigrants who migrate to these regions of the world bring foreign ways of living in harmony that are often influential and attractive. This is why immigration laws are becoming more strict. Those in power fear a sense of culture could collapse their unjust regimes.

Spiritual ceremonies practiced in other cultures that incorporate plant medicines such as ayahuasca, iboga and peyote stimulate the birth of creativity and shatter manufactured belief systems – paving the way for fresh new paradigms. Love culture can overpower all injustice.

"The world in which you were born is just one model of reality. Other cultures are not failed attempts at being you, they are unique manifestations of the human spirit." – Wade Davis, *Light At the Edge of the World*

Beyond what public school systems, media outlets, and societal structures have manufactured there is a culture rooted in pure intention. This is a culture where minds have not been compromised by lies that are disguised as history, mainstream news, scientific discoveries, corporate education, traditions or norms. Free thinking people who are immune to manipulation of their dignity embrace the vastness of living congruent with our innate connection to nature.

There is a universal refusal to be governed by those who generate motivation from what makes less of us and are disconnected from their inherent ability to reason. Those who adapt this way of life refuse to obey orders or commands from tyrants who have been stripped of all goodness, and decline to be controlled by the parasitic consciousness which circulates around masses of humans who lack awareness.

Love culture contributes in no way to the suffering of other forms of vibrant energy, and is not depleting of our resources or the harmony needed to maintain peace. There are good folks interspersed among the chaos, confusion, and delusions who know no crime, experience no disease, and are thriving from plant-based purity.

Rene Dubos states in his book, *Man Adapting* (1), that *culture signifies what people do as result of being taught*. All of the incongruities, restlessness, and distasteful behavior we adapt is associated with buying into a negligent system that has been devised by profiteers. The old paradigm teaches failure and hatred. The rising culture leads with love and grace.

"The 'norm' for humanity is love. Brutality is an aberration. We are not sinners by nature. We learn to be bad. We are taught to stray from our good paths. We are made to be crazy by other people who are also crazy, and who draw a map of the world which is fearful, negative and ugly." – Jack Forbes, Columbus and Other Cannibals

Merging Leaders

There must be equal distribution of land mass among animals and people. In the United States there are 2.3 billion acres of land and just over three-hundred million citizens. To divide the land equally would provide each person with a little over seven acres of land. With this acreage, each citizen would be expected to care for the land, grow their own food, and contribute to the process of planetary regeneration. This is not a call for Socialism, this is a plea for clean air, healthy food, potent soil and pure water.

The current paradigm rewards livestock with large areas of land, and materially and resourcefully enriches a small percentage of people with assets, while neglecting the larger majority. Those who are not among the ruling class are subjected to destruction, poisoning, poverty and sickness. The time has come for those holding the staff to dissolve corruption, end planetary degradation, and work toward cleaning up the mess they carefully crafted.

As oil companies and multinational corporations take control by uprooting, unearthing, and being unruly, they also possess a capability to foster goodness and supplement the expansion of light. Purity does not reject those who seek a merging of colors, collaboration of cultures, and universal peace. Those who exploit and manipulate nature for profit could learn from wisdom how to gain abundance in conservation. Treasures of the most high can only be found in preserving what enriches us at a soulular level.

Earth always remains secure in her spirit. By exploiting her we only steal vitality from children, future generations, and ourselves. A simple solution for restoring balance would be the willful relinquishing of control by those who are influential. Leaders from each generation can hold meetings and formulate ways to live with equality, fairness and peace. The commonality being sought after would apply to the betterment of humanity, not for the profits of corporations and individuals. We need to reconnect with Gaia, and work together to enrich and nourish the soul of nature.

Attuning To Gaia's Frequency

"When you realize Earth is so much more than simply your environment, you will be moved to protect her in the same way as yourself. This is the awareness we need. The future of the planet depends on whether we are able to cultivate this insight or not. Earth and all species on Earth are in real danger. If we can develop a deep relationship with Earth, we will have enough love, strength and awakening in order to change our way of life." – Thich Nhat Hanh

The miraculous human body was crafted meticulously with precision and exactitude. Components necessary for longevity and optimal functioning require dietary purity and a pristine lifestyle. We were not created with flaws. The health implications we experience are proportioned with what we choose to ingest, what is injected into us through syringes, and the contaminants permeating the environment around us. Our disconnect from sunlight dims our shine.

When we attune to Gaia's frequency we are able to essentially live free from disease and suffering. To synchronize in this way with Earth's spirit we are required to coexist in perfect harmony with all sentient beings and honor all life force. The most erroneous action adapted by man is the practice of raising and killing animals for food. Animals are not here for us to ingest. Their flesh is poison to our cells. We are to leave them alone and not afflict them with any harm.

In addition to eating meat and dairy products, man is also plagued with the extensive presence of chemicals. Nearly every home occupied by man is filled with cleaning chemicals, air fresheners, and furniture coated in flame retardants. Harmful pharmaceutical pills are often stored in cabinets. Faucets pump out fluoridated water, and lawns are saturated with glyphosate and other chemicals. To harmonize with Gaia, no harmful chemicals can be in our sphere. We must embrace the perfection of being human and abstain from depending on immunization shots and vaccines to enhance immunity. We have to restore our faith in nature as a guardian and protector, and stop relying on corporations to feed us.

Ingesting Vibrant Foods

"Keeping your body healthy is an expression of gratitude to the whole cosmos – trees, clouds, everything." – Thich Nhat Hanh

Food is an element. Like air, earth, fire and water, food is essential for survival. For our diet to enhance well-being, the foods we ingest must be of the highest radiant frequency. To attune to Gaia's level of frequency we are expected to eat living foods. By *living* I am referring to fresh, organic fruits, nuts, seeds and vegetables that have not been cooked, pasteurized or altered in any way that can damage nutrient content. If a food requires cooking, meaning the food is not edible unless cooked, this is not ideal for eating. When you eat food you are more inclined to be drawn to the food source. By choosing to eat fruits, vegetables and other plant-based foods this connects us to nature – the origin of that food. The living energy rewards us with more life. Ultimately we change the course of our evolution. When we eat food made in a lab, or manufactured in a factory, this directs us away from nature and we often drift toward embracing what is unnatural.

In his book, *The Secret Life of Plants (2)*, Peter Tomkins shares the fascinating story of a French scientist named Andre Bovis who in the early 1900's designed a tool used for measuring vitality known as the *Bovis Scale*. The device has since been referred to as a *Biotensor*. Using angstroms as the measuring unit, he was able to measure energy wavelengths of food, humans and plants on a level of zero (lowest possible frequency) to ten-thousand (highest possible frequency).

In the 1930's a man named Andre Simoneton followed up his work. Simoneton was a scientist and expert of electromagnetism. After falling ill he revived his vitality eating foods measured at the highest frequency on the *Bovis Scale*. He began to conduct studies on energetics of food and their impact on human energy levels. Energy emitted from the human body was detected in a range from 6,200 to 7,000 angstroms. Healthy individuals maintain a frequency of 6,500 or higher. What these men discovered is those who are ill, or especially stricken with cancer and other diseases, are below this level. Some with cancer measured as low as 4,875. To raise this level, as Simoneton was able to accomplish within his own body, high vibrational foods must be eaten, and foods measuring at a low frequency need to be eliminated from the diet. In addition to abstaining from ingesting poor quality food, deleterious lifestyle habits are also to be avoided.

Both Bovis and Simoneton categorized foods on four levels according to their angstrom measurement. Raw fruits and vegetables ranged from 8,000 to 10,000 – being the highest. Interestingly, organic produce free of chemicals tested higher than conventional. Levels were reduced by one-third after transportation from the garden to supermarket. After cooking, levels dropped another third. Foods that measured between 3,000 and 6,500 angstroms included cooked vegetables, fish, sugarcane and wine. Cheese, coffee, cooked meats, milk chocolate and boiled teas each scored below 3,000. At zero, bleached flour, liquor, margarine, refined sugar and all pasteurized items contained no radiant energy whatsoever. Raw cow's milk fresh from the udder tested at 6,500 angstroms, yet after being bottled for only twenty-four hours the energy levels dropped by ninety percent. After pasteurization, milk consistently leveled out at zero. Fruit and vegetable juices also dropped to zero after pasteurization. Once rehydrated, energy levels of sun-dried and dehydrated fruits did not change.

From these findings we learn there is more to food than simply eating for calories, fat, protein and vitamins. We begin to understand the meaning of life-force energy. The information presented from their studies explains why we cannot *enrich* or *fortify* truly *dead* foods with nutrients and expect to get much benefit from eating these products. To gain the most energy possible from food, eating raw fruits and vegetables is essential and imperative.

"When you nourish your mind and spirit you feed the soul of life. When you improve yourself, you improve the lives of those around you. When you advance confidently in the direction of your dreams, you begin to draw upon the power of the universe." – Robin Sharma, *Daily Inspiration*

Enzymes in live foods aid digestion. Living foods contain life within them and promote cellular longevity. A sprout is a perfect example of this type of food. All nutrients in sprouts are unharmed and ready to provide the body with clean energy. Other living foods are raw fruits and vegetables. Fresh, unpasteurized green juices and smoothies are also considered *living*.

We produce around two-hundred thousand new cells every second of our lives. Our bodies are made up of trillions of cells. Each is an individual living organism. Among the cells main concerns are protecting and contributing to the health of other cells. Our cells keep us alive, and we should do our best to nourish them for the span of time they live within us. When we fail to nourish our cells, they do not provide us with optimal health. Think of owning a business. To keep your employees happy you must compensate them. Now, say you stop paying them and keep making them work. How long do you expect them to continue working? Imagine your cells as employees battling to keep your business intact and their form of payment is nourishing food. Be sure you pay them well.

Even the cells of the healthiest people in the world die off at some point. Every minute their bodies are generating millions of new cells. These cells are constructed from the energy and substances present in their system. With eating richly nourishing food, we provide the high-vibrational energy needed for cellular regeneration. When we cheat and eat poor quality foods we are punished with mutated cells. Abusing drugs, drinking alcohol, shopping at convenience stores, gas stations and pharmacies, smoking cigarettes, taking prescription medications and pills, and using unnatural cosmetic, hygienal and suncare products on your skin also depletes vitality. The radiant frequency of chemicals, drugs and poisons is not detectable from being so low.

People who commonly eat clarified sugars, cooked oils, dairy, eggs, fast and processed foods, meat, synthetic chemicals, and other food-like substances – while also drinking alcohol, energy drinks and soda – tend to have bodies composed of weak cells prone to disease. By choosing to ingest substances that possess zero radiant frequency, their bones are being depleted of nourishment, and organ tissues are accumulating residues of these unhealthy foods. Those following such harmful diets end up being visibly depressed and unhealthy with complexions lacking the vibrancy they would have from fueling with truly healthy foods. To reverse sadness and stimulate happiness we want to build cells using optimal fuel sources. These fuel sources are raw, organic fruits, vegetables and plant-based foods – or living foods.

"My focus each day is to be myself, live my true passions, inspire greater health, and wear my soul shamelessly with strength and grace." – Kristina Carrillo-Bucaram, *Fully Raw*

Always aim to eat food containing nutrients in their natural spectrum without alteration. The reason we eat food – aside from the obvious of satiating hunger – is to nourish cells, organs, tissues and blood, and to fuel our brain. We gain this nourishment from nutrients within the particular foods we eat. Macronutrients (proteins, fats, carbohydrates) as well as micronutrients (vitamins, minerals, antioxidants, water, bioflavonoids, biophotons, etc) are equally important for overall bodily function. The micronutrients however, are vital in the production of enzymes, and help these proteins carry out their important duties within the body.

Enzymes from raw foods control most metabolic processes in the body. Once food is heated over a certain temperature, which varies for each food, enzymes are denatured. The body is then required to draw upon enzymatic stores to break down food. By eating more raw foods we conserve energy consuming the life-force provided. This energy can also be measured in biophotons. Biophotons are absorbed into fruits, vegetables and other plant-based foods from the sun. When we eat these foods in their natural state, we also absorb the energy of the sun. This is why eating raw nurtures healthy glowing skin, improves mental clarity, and helps our brain to function optimally.

Despite losing a vast amount of nutrition during the cooking process, some nutrients can become more bio-available when lightly steamed. While eating a diet rich in raw fruits and vegetables can easily be maintained, incorporating steamed choices can also be of benefit.

In addition to ingesting high-vibrational foods, various plant medicines from the rainforest are rich in life-force energy. Being out in nature increases frequency. Walking barefoot in forests, swimming in clean rivers, and gardening are all potent for heightening vigor. Prayer is also an effective way to elevate our radiance. No matter what we eat we can use the power of prayer and intention to bless food and water. Blessings are a powerful remedy to transform anything we consume – especially foods of less nutritional value – into something healthier and more nourishing for our body. If you are in a position where you have no choice but to eat unhealthy food, such as being incarcerated or hospitalized, bless your meals with good intention and prayer.

As we familiarize with the rhythms of Mother Earth, and acclimatize to her pulsations, we improve our quality of living while also relieving her of the burdens attached to endorsing manufactured culture. Our ability to redefine our heritage, renew the values we abide by, and revive morality must be utilized with more proficiency. We cannot allow corporations to poison us any longer. We are being summoned to remove alcohol, cigarettes, fast food and pills from tribal reservations and bring health back to our tribes. When I emancipated myself from the corporate food chain, I was immediately rewarded with a stronger spiritual connection to nature and my higher power.

Our duties as soldiers of humanity include growing a diverse range of edible plants with grace and tenderness for the land being occupied, protecting wild animals and plant species, and improving the planet any way we can. Choosing to buy products that inflict wounds on the land we depend on for survival, ingest drugs and pills that deplete vitality, and give up our inherent right to good health to government organizations and corporations is not reflective of being an Earth warrior.

Man was created to eat in alliance with the plant Kingdom, not in defiance of nature. For us to flourish and shine we need to give up harmful addictions and choose to eat in alignment with our anatomy. Once we adapt to eating this way we reestablish our connection with nature. As we heal our conditions within, our focus then shifts to planetary healing and restoration of nature.

Eating In Alignment With Our Anatomy

Compounds in plants constituting the life force within them – anthocyanins, antioxidants, bioflavonoids, biophotons, cells, minerals, phytonutrients, polyphenols, vitamins and water – are not damaged when harvested. Only after cooking, oxidization, or processing do we lose the energy in plant-derived foods. By eating plants we continue the cycle of life. When animals are killed, the life force within them dies. The flesh immediately begins to decompose. This is why meat manufacturers inject their product with preservatives and food coloring agents to alter appearance. Once inside the human body, meat produces harmful metabolites and byproducts that contribute to cancer and other disease. Plants help generate neurotransmitters, feed healthy bacteria, and aid our bodily systems to assure healthy organ functioning. Eating fruits, picked green leaf vegetables, seeds, nuts and a limited amount of certain grain-like foods does not require the killing or uprooting of any plant. We are not harming the planet, or plant, by eating this way.

A common widespread belief is we must raise animals for food to receive optimal amounts of calcium, iron, protein, zinc and other nutrients from their flesh and secretions. This is false. These animals get their calcium, iron, protein and other nutrients from eating a variety of grasses and plants. This generates lean muscle. The same is true for humans who restrict meat from their diet and only consume plants. They are naturally lean and strong.

There is not a single nutrient our body demands that we cannot obtain while eating a plant-based diet free of harmful animal proteins. We receive protein and fat when we eat animals and their by-products, however we miss out on antioxidants, fiber, phytonutrients and other important micronutrients lacking in animal-based foods. We also ingest carcinogenic compounds such as heterocyclic amines and polycyclic aromatic hydrocarbons; damage our endothelial cells with TMAO, trans-fats and dietary cholesterol; increase our risk of developing cancer and being sickened from microbial pathogens through the mammalian meat molecule known as Neu5Gc; and disrupt digestive and eliminative processes in our body.

While cholesterol is paramount for our body to function, we create more than enough of the healthy version as we nourish ourselves with plant-based foods. Foreign cholesterol obtained from eating meat, dairy and eggs is not the cholesterol we want in our system. By eating a well-balanced vegan diet, our body will produce the healthy version in abundance.

Ingesting fiber is significantly important for maintaining an untainted bowel. Fibrous vegetables contain high levels of inulin, which feeds healthy actinobacteria in our gut. Animal-based foods contain zero fiber. Antioxidants and phytonutrients help to maintain a healthy microbiome, eliminate free radicals, lengthen telomeres, and fight off harmful pathogens. These nutrients are non-existent in meat, dairy and eggs. Because we get more than enough protein in our diet by eating a combination of raw fruits, vegetables, nuts and seeds, continuing to eat animal-based foods is unnecessary. On a plant-based diet we also receive sufficient amounts of calcium, iron and other essential nutrients. The only vitamins we may need to supplement with are B-12 and D. Keep in mind that more meat-eaters suffer from B-12 deficiencies than vegans so this is not a *vegan deficiency*. *Sun Is Shining* superfood is a good choice of supplement for assuring you receive a full spectrum of nutrition on a plant-based diet.

From an anatomical perspective, humans are not designed to be omnivorous. In fact, our anatomical design resembles that of a frugivore or herbivore. We have small canine teeth to tear apart the cellulose fibers in vegetables. Omnivorous animals use their fangs and sharp teeth to break down bones and cartilage. We do not have claws that can penetrate flesh or harm animals – we have soft, porous nails for peeling fruit. We are equipped with a long, plant-friendly digestive tract. Omnivores have short tracts allowing for them to digest and excrete animal-derived food sources easily. We sweat through pores in our skin while omnivores sweat through the tongue and have minimal sweat glands. Our salivary chemistry is alkaline while an omnivorous animals is acidic. Our body requires fiber to stimulate peristalsis, an omnivores does not. Our brain chemistry is fueled by glycogen while an omnivore requires fats and proteins for brain functioning. We even see in full color-scale like other herbivores and frugivores – omnivores and carnivores do not. Every component of our anatomy supports the notion we are not omnivorous or carnivorous mammals. We were simply not created to eat meat. All evidence points directly to us being put here on Earth to eat fruit, some leafy green vegetables, and nothing else other than the occasional nuts, seeds and sprouts.

The article, *Evolution and Prostate Cancer,* was featured in the Winter 2000 edition of the *Prostate Cancer Update* journal *(3).* Lead author and scientist, Don Coffey, explains how i*n nature animals that are carnivores – meat-eaters like lions – do not have seminal vesicles. The only animals that have both prostates and seminal vesicles are herbivores – veggie-eating animals like bulls, apes, and elephants. We are the huge glaring exception to this rule: Men have seminal vesicles, too. In other words, man – a meat-lover – has the makeup of an animal that should be vegetarian. The fact that men eat meat seems to be a mistake that nature never accounted for.* We seem to be the only mammal with seminal vesicles consciously choosing to indulge in animal-derived foods. We are also the only mammal who develops prostate cancer.

In an October 2008 publication in the peer-reviewed *Nutrition In Clinical Practice* journal (4), Dr. William C. Roberts explains how carnivorous and omnivorous animals do not develop atherosclerosis. These animals can eat endless amounts of fat and cholesterol and their arteries will not clog up. In studies on herbivorous animals however, atherosclerosis was easily produced when monkeys, rabbits and rats were fed high-cholesterol, high-saturated fat diets comprised of eggs and meat. Humans choosing to eat animal-derived foods are experiencing an epidemic of atherosclerosis. There is a reason why true carnivores do not develop this condition while humans continue to suffer from atherosclerosis.

Whether we are frugivorous, herbivorous or omnivorous – beyond arguing over what we were created to eat – we cannot deny the harsh fact that meat consumption is killing humanity. Excess animal protein and cooked meat carcinogens such as heterocyclic amines and polycyclic aromatic hydrocarbons are linked to many degenerative diseases. These include: Alzheimer's; cancers of the breast, colon, prostate, and female anatomy; cardiovascular disease; diabetes; erectile dysfunction; macular degeneration; multiple sclerosis and osteoporosis. Dietary cholesterol and saturated fats are damaging endothelial cells lining the circulatory system. Trimethylamine oxide (TMAO) – a metabolite generated when bacteria in the gut digest choline sourced from chicken, eggs, and fish and L-carnitine found in red meat – seriously damages blood vessels. Malignant tumors are forming from a mammalian molecule known as Neu5Gc, found in most animal-derived foods. Infectious diseases are spreading through the food supply. Never before have we been so plagued with sickness.

Addiction to flesh foods is the Achilles heel sabotaging the human species. Meat consumption is carcinogenic, health degrading, and can be directly linked to nearly every disease afflicting man. Somewhere on the path of human evolution we were led astray into adapting the habit of eating flesh foods. While in some regions of the world our ancestors relied on meat for survival, today with advances in technology and transportation, we no longer need to exploit animals for food. We are smarter now, and have a wide enough variety of plant-based foods available to diversify our palate and consider meat obsolete.

In his book, *Meatonomics* (5), author David Robinson Simon alerts us of *programs managed by the US Department of Agriculture spending $550 million annually on advertisements and slogans encouraging American citizens to eat more meat and meat products.* Mr. Simon also informs us of *the American government spending $38 billion each year to subsidize the meat and dairy industries, while only 0.04 percent of this amount (i.e., $17 million) is going toward subsidizing fruits and vegetables.* As multinational corporations and government organizations use industry propaganda to continually drill us with misleading nutritional information, trying desperately to keep us buried in an unsustainable way of life, we are slowly beginning to manifest a universal awakening.

Human intelligence is claiming superiority over the dying hierarchy that has dictated our well being for far too long. With the aid of research science we now have enough evidence to support the notion that meat is deadly. We must share this news.

There is a sialic acid sugar molecule known as N-glycolylneuraminic acid, or Neu5Gc, that cannot be synthesized by humans. This molecule binds to cells lining hollow organs and blood vessels. According to a May 2010 study in *PNAS* journal (6), this cellular-surfaced molecule is incorporated into human tissues from eating animal-derived foods. Dietary Neu5Gc tends to accumulate particularly in epithelial cells lining hollow organs where carcinomas develop, or in the endothelium lining blood vessels where atherosclerosis occurs. Once present in the body our immune system develops anti-Neu5Gc antibodies, and because this molecule attaches to endothelial and epithelial cells, the antibodies attack these cells. This immune response leads to chronic inflammation and is likely responsible for the high frequency of diet-related carcinomas and other human diseases.

In a January 2015 PNAS journal study (7), researchers *used an improved method to survey common foods for free and glycosidically bound forms of the nonhuman sialic acid N-glycolylneuraminic acid (Neu5Gc).* Results displayed evidence of this molecule being *highly and selectively enriched in red meat.* The research team discovered *the bound form of Neu5Gc is bioavailable, undergoing metabolic incorporation into human tissues, despite being a foreign antigen.* Interactions of this antigen with circulating anti-Neu5Gc antibodies were found to promote inflammation and accelerate tumor growth. This carcinogenic compound is found primarily in beef, pork, lamb, egg and milk products – with trace amounts present in fish.

A September 2016 *Glycoconjugate Journal (8)* study documents evidence of a *non-human sialic acid sugar molecule called Neu5Gc – commonly found in red meat – having the potential to increase tumor formations when consumed.* This *UC Davis School of Medicine study examined presence of the acid in pig meat and found that pig organs, including the lungs, heart, spleen, kidney, and liver, had the highest concentrations.* Results showed risk factors associated with consuming Neu5Gc are significantly increased when the organs are cooked and therefore researchers assert, *dietary consumption of organ meats should be discouraged to protect against cancer, cardiovascular, and other inflammatory diseases.*

Dating all the way back to May 1962, a study was published in the *Journal of Biological Chemistry* (9) finding all influenza A viruses were dependent on Neu5Gc as a binding receptor to connect with cells. Fifty years later, in the *Annals of the New York Academy of Sciences*, this discovery was elongated. An April 2012 study *(10)* explains how viruses contain glycoproteins that bind to sialic acids on the surface of human cells and cell membranes of the upper respiratory tract. Judging from the information in these studies, we could greatly reduce our chances of contracting a virus by eliminating animal-derived foods containing Neu5Gc. Rather than inoculating the body with viruses through administration of influenza vaccines, a safer and more logical way to protect yourself from the influenza virus could be choosing to eat vegan.

An August 2010 study in the *Journal of Experimental Medicine* (11) introduces the term xenosialitis. This describes *the interaction between non-human Neu5Gc and circulating Neu5Gc antibodies resulting in chronic inflammation that promotes carcinogenesis and atherogenesis.* Researchers examined infants to determine when anti-Neu5Gc antibodies develop in the body. Their findings indicate a lack of the production of anti-Neu5Gc IgG antibodies at three months when their diets were devoid of Neu5Gc. Soon after the introduction of Neu5Gc in the diet, in the form of cow's milk formula and baby foods containing red meat, the levels began to rise. This highlights how introducing animal-derived foods to children can be detrimental to their health.

A May 2016 *Mayo Clinic* study (12), *Is Meat Killing Us?*, presents more evidence supporting the surety of meat increasing mortality rates. *Mortality rates for red meat-eaters were found to be higher for all causes of death. The study observed one million individuals across the United States, Europe, and China during a period of five to twenty-eight years – in addition to cross-referencing thirteen cohort studies that included 1.5 million people – and found consumption of red meat, processed or not, led to higher mortality risks across illnesses including heart disease and cancer.* This was published in the *Journal of the American Osteopathic Association.* Researchers concluded, *"Despite variability in data, the evidence is consistent that increased intake of red meat, especially processed red meat, is associated with increased all-cause mortality. Red meat also increases cardiovascular disease and cancer mortality in Western cohorts. A vegan diet has been shown to improve several parameters of health, including reversal of cardiovascular disease, decreased body mass index (BMI), decreased risk of diabetes, and decreased blood pressure."* The study suggests *avoidance of red and processed meats and a diet rich in plant-based whole foods including fruits, vegetables, whole grains, nuts, and legumes* as a *sound, evidence-based recommendation.*

Heart disease is mostly attributed to poor diet. An early phenomenon of atherosclerosis and heart disease is endothelial dysfunction. A study featured in the November 1997 *Circulation* journal *(13)* introduces the association between dietary cholesterol and impaired endothelium dependent vasodilation. Vasodilation refers to the widening of blood vessels. The endothelium is a thin layer of cells covering the inner surface of the arteries – separating circulating blood from tissues. In this study, dietary cholesterol levels in what is considered the *normal* range were linked to decreased vasodilation and endothelium dysfunction. As more cholesterol is ingested in the diet, endothelial cells are further damaged, atherosclerotic deposits begin to form, and heart disease transpires.

Dietary cholesterol is found only in animal-based foods. In the *China Study,* Dr. T. Colin Campbell studied the dietary effects on blood cholesterol levels and determined that *animal protein consumption by men was associated with increasing levels of 'bad' blood cholesterol, whereas plant protein consumption was associated with decreasing levels of this same cholesterol (14).* This tells us we should avoid animal products if we want to lower our cholesterol levels and prevent heart disease. Simply restricting calories will not prevent disease from occurring. We have to abide by clean diets free of chemicals to assure good health.

In addition to dietary cholesterol contributing to atherosclerosis because of impaired endothelium function, an oxide known as trimethylamine oxide (TMAO), has also been discovered to promote heart disease. In the May 2013 *Nature Medicine* journal, a study (15) was released documenting how bacteria in our gut metabolize L-carnitine – a nutrient found in fish, meat, milk and poultry – into TMAO. These same bacteria also break down choline from eggs and high-fat dairy products into TMAO. When dietary choline and L-carnitine are ingested by bacteria in the intestines, they are metabolized into trimethylamine (TMA). Once TMA enters the liver, an enzyme converts the compound to TMAO, which penetrates the bloodstream, *alters whole-body cholesterol metabolism, promotes vascular inflammation and causes formation of unstable plaques in arterial walls.* In this study, TMAO accelerated the development of atherosclerosis. Vegan and vegetarian subjects were also included in this research and found to produce less TMAO following ingestion of isolated L-carnitine. Scientists have discovered carnitine and choline from plant-derived foods do not generate production of TMAO when metabolized by bacteria in the gut, as forms of these nutrients sourced from meat, dairy or eggs have demonstrated.

An additional study in the November 2014 *Cell Metabolism* journal (16) introduced a separate metabolite of L-carnitine known as γ-butyrobetaine. This intermediate byproduct of meat digestion is formed in abundant amounts by microbes in the gut and converted into TMA – eventually forming TMAO. Not only does TMAO damage blood vessels, in January 2015, *Circulation Research* journal published a study (17) documenting the capability of this metabolite to *contribute to progressive renal fibrosis and dysfunction.* Patients with chronic kidney disease (CKD) were also found to have elevated plasma TMAO levels – suggesting a link between CKD and meat consumption.

A study in the March 2016 *Cell* journal *(18)* shows how scientists are able to predict incidence risks for thrombotic events in human subjects stemming from elevated TMAO levels. The paper explains how *normal platelet function is critical for healthy blood flow, while heightened platelet reactivity is associated with cardiometabolic diseases and enhanced potential for thrombotic events.* This study successfully demonstrates how generation of TMAO *directly contributes to* heart disease. Most recently, a prospective cohort study conducted at the *Cleveland Clinic* and published in the October 2016 *Journal of the American heart Association (19)* found elevated TMAO levels were associated with a 2.7-fold increased mortality risk in patients with peripheral artery disease (PAD). This was discovered after *examining the relationship between fasting plasma TMAO and all-cause mortality over five years among 821 consecutive patients with adjudicated PAD.* The only way to avoid this deadly metabolite is to abstain from eating animal-derived foods.

In a video released in January 2013 on *nutritionfacts.org*, *PhIP: The Three-Strikes Breast Carcinogen (20)*, Dr. Greger discusses heterocyclic amines and how PhIP is one of the most abundant heterocyclic amines in cooked meat. These carcinogenic compounds are formed at high temperatures from the reaction between creatine or creatinine, amino acids, and sugar in meat, dairy, and egg products. PhIP is nearly impossible to avoid for those who indulge in animal-derived foods because the toxin is found in many commonly consumed cooked meats – particularly chicken, beef, and fish. After absorption of PhIP, the compound is converted to a genotoxic metabolite in the liver – becoming more likely to cause DNA mutation, trigger cancer, and promote tumor growth. In a 2009 *Mutagenesis Journal (21) study,* researchers discovered ingestion of PhIP causes DNA mutation that may initiate tumor growth, promotes cancer due to potent estrogenic activity, and promotes the invasiveness of breast cancer cells. Abstaining from dairy, eggs, and meat is the safest way to evade this amine, and is a method of prevention for living cancer free.

A March 2005 *Chemical Research in Toxicology* study (22) was published finding more than twenty heterocyclic amines in cooked meats, fish, and poultry prepared under common household cooking conditions. This includes baking, boiling, broiling, frying, grilling, sauteing, and smoking. Urine samples from subjects eating meat were found to contain high levels of PhIP and other health degrading heterocyclic compounds. Even those who refrained from eating meat, yet still included boiled eggs or cheese in their diet, showed traces of these compounds.

Many of these heterocyclic and polycyclic compounds found in grilled meats are also present in cigarettes. In fact, some grilled meats can be more abundant in pyrenes and other polycyclic compounds than cigarettes. In a comparative risks analysis study, *one piece of grilled steak was found to contain the equivalent carcinogenic load as six-hundred cigarettes.* This is comparable to smoking a pack a day for thirty days each time a steak is eaten. This information was presented decades ago in a study – *Metabolism of Polycyclic Compounds (23)* – published in the February 1964 *Biochemical Journal.* The main source of these carcinogens in grilled meats are polycyclic aromatic hydrocarbons. Polycyclic compounds are *highly carcinogenic atmospheric pollutants formed by incomplete combustion of carbon-containing fuels such as coal, tar, wood, fat, tobacco, and incense.* When fat and juices from meat drip over the heat source – causing flames – these flames then adhere to the surface of the meat. Multiple studies have shown that high levels of these hydrocarbons are found in cooked foods – particularly in meats cooked at high temperatures, such as with grilling or barbecuing – and in smoked fish. When we consider the vast amount of people who smoke and eat steak regularly, we begin to understand why heart disease and cancer are so prevalent.

In the October 2015 edition of *The Lancet Oncology* journal, the *International Agency for Research on Cancer* (IARC) published a report (24) providing evidence of processed meats and red meats being strongly correlated with colorectal, pancreatic, and prostate cancers. These processed meats include bacon, deli cold cuts, ham, hot dogs, pepperoni, salami, and sausage. Beef, goat, lamb, and pork can all be considered red meats. In the analysis, eating fifty grams a day of processed meats was found to increase the risk of developing colon cancer by up to eighteen percent. Red meats were found to be associated with greater susceptibility to cancers of the breast, colon, pancreas, and prostate. These findings prompted the *World Health Organization* to classify all processed and red meats as probable carcinogens – substances known to cause cancer.

Advanced glycation end-products (AGEs) tend to shorten telomeres, accelerating the aging process. Glucose binds to cooked animal proteins, leading to the formation of AGEs, and by eating meat we damage our cells and shorten telomeres. In a September 2013 study led by Dr. Dean Ornish and published in *The Lancet Oncology* journal (25), researchers determined changes in diet, exercise, stress management, and social support can result in longer telomeres – the parts of chromosomes that affect aging. For five years, researchers followed thirty-five men with localized, early-stage prostate cancer to explore the relationship between comprehensive lifestyle changes, and telomere length and telomerase activity. All the men were closely monitored through screening and biopsies. Ten of the patients embarked on lifestyle changes that included: a plant-based diet (high in fruits, vegetables and unrefined grains, and low in fat and refined carbohydrates); moderate exercise (walking thirty minutes a day, six days a week); and stress reduction (gentle yoga-based stretching, breathing, meditation). They were compared to the other twenty-five study participants who were not asked to make major lifestyle changes.

When the five-year study ended, *the group that made the lifestyle changes experienced a significant increase in telomere length of approximately ten percent.* Researchers found that *the more people changed their behavior by adhering to the recommended lifestyle program, the more dramatic their improvements in telomere length.* Meanwhile, *the men in the control group who were not asked to alter their lifestyle had measurably shorter telomeres – nearly three percent shorter.* This study demonstrates how we can slow the aging process by choosing to eat plant-based, exercising, and eliminating stress.

In addition to accelerating aging, eating animal-based foods such as meat, dairy, and eggs, is strongly associated with depression. This is likely because of the arachadonic acid contained within these foods – along with the low-level energy, and harmful pathogens. A February 2012 *Nutrition Journal* study (26) found by simply eliminating animal products from the diet of omnivore subjects their mood improved within two weeks. Researchers discovered arachadonic acid – found primarily in chicken and eggs – was to blame for their initial depression before the elimination of these foods. They acknowledged arachadonic acid as a compound that can *adversely impact mental health via a cascade of brain inflammation.* High intakes of this acid began to promote changes in the brain that resulted in disturbed mood and this was demonstrated with the group of subjects who continued to eat fish for the duration of the study. Fish-eaters reported significantly worse moods than vegans. The conclusion was *restricting meat, fish, and poultry improved short-term mood state in modern omnivores.* Main sources for arachadonic acid are chicken, eggs, beef, processed meats (sausage, hot dogs, bacon, and ribs), fish, burgers, cold cuts, pork, and pizza. If you are unhappy, and your diet is abundant in these foods, perhaps consider adapting some dietary changes. Try skipping meat once or twice a week to start, and then progress to removing animal-derived foods entirely from your diet. You will be thankful once you transition.

A January 2014 *Nature* journal study *(27)* explains how long-term dietary intake influences activities of the trillions of microorganisms residing in the human gut. These same microorganisms communicate with our brain and have an impact on our appetite, behavior, feelings, and mood. Researchers studied the impact animal-based diets and plant-based diets have on the gut microbiota by dividing the groups into vegan, or strictly meat-based diets. In the study, the research team found, *Short-term consumption of diets composed entirely of animal products alters the microbial community structure and overwhelms inter-individual differences in microbial gene expression. The animal-based diet was found to increase the activity of bilophilia wadsworthia, showing a link between dietary fat, bile acids, and the outgrowth of microorganisms capable of triggering inflammatory bowel disease.*

Bilophilia are microbes that love bile. Because bile helps to digest fats, more bile is produced when a diet is rich in meat, dairy and eggs. When extra bile is produced, we generate more of these microbes. Blooms of bilophilia are known to cause inflammation and colitis – conditions closely associated with depression. In this study, researchers observed fifty clustered, species-level bacterial phylotypes and the impact of each diet. Among those eating plant-based diets, only three of these bacterial clusters were altered, while twenty-two of the phylotypes on animal-based diets were changed significantly. *The microbiome of those on meat-based diets had clusters composed of putrefactive microbes, bilophilia wadsworthia, increased lactic acid bacteria, staphylococcus, increased enteric deoxycholic acid concentrations (DCA), and several other potentially damaging organisms.* DCA is a secondary bile acid that promotes liver cancer, DNA damage, and hepatic carcinomas. A high level of bilophilia wadsworthia is known to cause bowel inflammation. This alteration in the gut microbiota can reflect as symptoms of anxiety and depression.

Justus Von Liebig was a German chemist who many consider as the founder of organic chemistry. He wrote in the 35th of *Letters On Chemistry* (28) about his experiments with bear and swine. When he fed bears bread and vegetables, the animals were calm and gentle. After feeding them meat for a few days they were ferocious. Swine that were fed meat had become so aggressive they would attack man. While science continues to provide evidence of how eating animal-derived foods negates good health, and our anatomical design is most closely aligned with a frugivorous or herbivorous animal, a surplus of misinformation continues to circulate around whether or not we should be eating meat.

We do not emerge from the womb craving flesh. In fact, no human child would ever look at an animal and perceive this being as a food source – as carnivores do naturally. We are influenced to start consuming meat by our parents, and the notion is ingrained in us as we mature. Most children are repulsed by the taste of milk and spit meat out when first introduced to the palate. Because industry propaganda has supplanted the preposterous idea in our mind that animal-derived foods are vital for development and growth, we force this way of life on our kids.

We are not born omnivores, we adapt to eating this way by means of cultural conditioning. The human body is miraculous, and through adaptation we still manage to sustain life eating in opposition of our anatomic design, but – as with any species who eats an unnatural diet – we eventually degenerate. We are seeing evidence today as the majority of our population is sickened and not well. The human adaptations allowing us to accommodate these foods in our diet are only possible through DNA mutations.

Choosing to disregard science, and unable to give up their addiction to meat, some who continue to eat animal-derived foods defend their habit by disseminating misleading information. They argue about their ancestors eating meat; how cavemen survived eating meat; that we need the animal protein, cholesterol, iron, and vitamin B12 in meat or we will die; how there will be an overpopulation of farm animals if we stop eating them; and they frequently provoke arguments insisting plants are also alive and by eating them we inflict the same pain on them as animals.

Under the lead of professor Fabian Kanz, a group of researchers from the *Department of Forensic Medicine* at the *Medical University of Vienna* in Austria conducted a study on bone samples from the remains of twenty-two men whose graves were unearthed from a gladiator cemetery in the ancient Roman city of Ephesus. The team analyzed the collagen and mineral content in these samples and discovered the men ate vegetarian diets consisting mostly of vegetables and grains. Gladiators from ancient Rome are widely believed to have been the strongest humans to ever inhabit Earth. This study (29), published in the October 2014 *PLOS One* journal – *Stable Isotope and Trace Element Studies on Gladiators and Contemporary Romans from Ephesus, Implications for Differences in Diet* – helps us to better understand our strength is generated from the nutrients provided by plants. There are no nutrients found in animal-derived foods not also abundant in foods sourced from plants.

As humans we share the responsibility of being caretakers of Earth. To perform this duty we are encouraged to be mindful of what foods we are ingesting and how they impact health. To grasp the concept of eating for vitality, we need to understand that dead foods are depleting and void of beneficial energy.

"There is not enough fish in the world's oceans to feed over six-billion human beings and another ten-billion domestic animals. This is why all of the world's commercial fisheries are collapsing. That is why whales, seals, dolphins and seabirds are starving. In a world fast losing resources of fresh water, having hundreds of millions of cows consuming over one-thousand gallons of water for every pound of beef produced is sheer lunacy." – Captain Paul Watson, *A Very Inconvenient Truth*

The Protein Myth

There is an antiquated misconception circulating around animal products, protein, and a plant-based lifestyle. For some strange reason most people carry a belief that animals are meat, and meat is protein. Using this perspective, when they confront those who choose to eat plant-based they always want to ask, *Where do you get your protein?* The fact so many people are clueless about what protein is, and have no idea where protein is derived from, displays how brainwashed society has become and how warped our nutritional knowledge truly is.

Asking a vegan where they get protein is like asking a tree where she gets oxygen. Protein comes from plants. This is knowledge we all must grasp. For those who choose to eat animals thinking this is an optimal protein source, they often fail to acknowledge the vegetarian animals they are eating receive their protein from eating grasses and various plant-derived foods. This is why cows, gorillas, horses, and land animals are naturally lean and strong. In fact, the only creature on land that is fat and lethargic happens to be the human species. Interestingly enough, we are the only land mammal not designed to eat meat who chooses to disobey their anatomical make-up and eat flesh. As a result we are afflicted with chronic disease, premature death and unnatural health conditions.

All plants are abundant in protein. To avoid sounding foolish, rather than asking those who eat plants where they get protein, we should question meat eaters about where they get antioxidants, carbohydrates, fiber, phytonutrients, and undamaged amino acids. By eating animal-derived foods the diet is void of these essential minerals, vitamins, and other nutrients.

To clarify, animals are not simply meat. They are not inanimate objects. The flesh of an animal is also not protein. While muscle tissues are constructed of proteins, these are not readily available proteins we can ingest and magically convert to the proteins we need for our species to function. Animal proteins are not highly bioavailable to humans – meaning we expend more energy metabolizing than we receive from eating them. Not only are we taxing our digestive and eliminative organs by choosing to eat animals for protein, we are also creating more of a protein deficiency because we have an excess of the wrong type of protein in our system. This is evident in the alarmingly high percentage of people who are obese. They are protein deficient because they are eating too much of the wrong proteins. As their eliminative organs get backed up further, they gain weight, develop acidosis and toxemia, and experience gut rot because they continue to add toxins faster than their bodies can process and expel them.

In the animal kingdom, naturally there is a custom of showing respect for those who move on by celebrating their lives. When other humans die, we traditionally arrange funeral services to honor their lives. When elephants pass, the rest of the herd will conduct a ceremony to appreciate their loved ones. With animal agriculture and the cycle of killing and eating animals, billions of chickens, cows, fish, lamb, pigs and turkeys are not being honored after they die. Rather than receiving a proper burial we choose to stuff parts of their dead corpses inside of our bellies. Essentially we use our bodies as graveyards for these animals. Our gut becomes a burial ground.

Digestion of flesh foods explains why we generate body odors and bad breath, and rely on chewing gum, colognes, deodorants and perfumes to mask the treacherous aroma coming from our insides. Bad breath and body odors come from a variety of compounds including bacteria, infected tonsils and glands, cancer, yeast and an overload of toxins and/or foreign substances including those along the alimentary tract. Putrefactive bacteria from meat, dairy, eggs and other chemicals Americans overload their bodies with are problematic for the eliminative and cardiovascular systems. They also leave behind a toxic residue. This residue helps to create odors and taints vitality, slowing and dulling the body systems. Even the strongest chewing gum and heaviest deodorant will not get to the root of this problem to cease the odors from returning. These residues and putrefactive bacteria can also create a perfect breeding environment for illness and disease. When I was eating animals during my earlier years of life my body odor and breath could be noticeable without chewing gum and deodorant. Today my diet is my odor neutralizer.

Meat is a poor source for amino acids we need to form protein. Once cooked, proteins in meat become denatured, and heat-sensitive amino acids are damaged. Because we require insulin to transport amino acids into the cells for the purpose of creating proteins, we also increase our risk for developing diabetes as we overload on animal proteins and saturate our bodies with refined sugars. Glucose is like a glue and practically glues itself to saturated fats, trans-fats and sulfur-containing amino acids that have been damaged by heat. As the insulin we produce tries to execute the primary function of transporting glucose and amino acids to the cells, these harmful fats and denatured proteins block the path because the glucose attaches to them, inhibiting penetration into the cells. To bypass this roadblock the pancreas secretes more insulin, and as the body continues to demand more, the pancreas gets weaker – eventually leading to pancreatic failure. For this reason we are encouraged to avoid animal fats and proteins if we aspire to maintain healthy pancreatic functioning and prevent diabetes.

While protein is important, we only need forty to eighty grams of protein a day in our diet, depending on our height, weight and how physically active we are. The *World Health Organization* (WHO) released a statement suggesting we consume 0.8 grams of protein per kilogram of body weight (30). For someone who weighs 120 pounds, this converts to forty-four grams of protein daily. For 150 pounds, this equals fifty-four grams a day. Those weighing 180 pounds require sixty-six grams of protein, and weighing in at 210 pounds would call for seventy-six grams. In *The Raw Food Nutrition Handbook (31)*, the Dina's explain how we easily exceed the WHO recommendations eating a plant-based diet rich in raw fruits and vegetables. Those abiding by the standard American, high-protein diet, are taking in too much protein – sometimes three to four times what various health organizations recommend as healthy or safe.

As a competitive athlete I always believed I needed extra protein to maintain lean muscle mass. I also thought this protein could only be sourced from animals. When I learned about plant proteins my performance improved.

Developing a protein deficiency while eating a plant-based diet rich in fruits and vegetables is nearly impossible. In fact, many of us have an over-abundant amount of protein in our bodies. In *Survival Into the 21st Century* (32), Viktoras Kulvinskas states: "*Protein in excess of our needs is not utilized by the body. Cooking meat also destroys the amino acids needed for building enzymes and healthy tissues. The protein is poorly absorbed and largely unavailable to cells. For these reasons, much of the protein we eat passes from the body, or is stored in tissues as waste.*" Ideally, we should not exceed any more than ten to twenty percent of our daily intake of calories from protein – unless we are competitive athletes. Many of us are exceeding this amount.

For every calorie of animal protein consumed, eleven times more fossil fuels are required than would be needed for a calorie of plant protein. To maintain an optimal level of health we must feed ourselves a colorful diet consisting of an array of fruits, nuts, seeds and vegetables. To achieve this elevated state of well-being, meat is not necessary, whey must be avoided, soy should be replaced with hemp protein, dairy needs to be recognized as food for cows not humans, and eggs cannot be ingested.

To learn more about adapting and maintaining a healthy plant-based lifestyle, please read my 2017 book, *Eating Plant-Based: The New Health Paradigm* (33). As we acquire this information about nutrition, and adapt to this way of life, we also need to be mindful of the chemicals permeating in our environment and home, and the healing benefits of sunlight. The combination of a plant-based diet, chemical-free lifestyle and sunlight therapy fills us with radiance and vitality.

"*All plants are our brothers and sisters. They talk to us, and if we can listen, we hear them. Before eating, always take time to thank them for the food. When we show our respect, they respond with respect for us in the form of nutrition.*" – Arapaho wisdom

Chemical Assault On Well-Being

A database maintained by the *American Chemical Society* *(34)* reports that humans have made or found over 150 million different chemicals on Earth. The *EPA* has identified eighty-five thousand chemicals under the *Toxic Substances Control Act* being used in commerce and this does not include those persisting in cosmetics, drugs, food additives, munitions, nuclear materials, pesticides and tobacco. This chemical pollution lowers Earth's frequency. If we wish to harmonize with Gaia we need to revive the purity on this planet and shift away from chemicals.

The average person in modern society fills their home with dangerous chemicals. Cabinets, pantries and refrigerators in nearly every house are filled with processed foods that contain cancer-causing chemicals and harmful ingredients. The majority of these foods are saturated with the chemical glyphosate, which has been linked in studies to several illnesses. Under the kitchen sink and in their bathrooms they store *beauty* products, cleaning supplies, cosmetics, detergents and toiletries that are toxic. They do not add filters to their faucets or shower heads. Quite often the water they consume is bottled and contains added ingredients. They use chewing gum, colognes, deodorants and perfumes to cover up odors that are reflective of a backed-up digestive system and poor bowel health. These cover-ups are also contaminated with industrial chemicals. They apply lip balms that contain parabens – which are strongly associated with breast cancer – to moisten their lips chapped from being deficient of essential nutrients. They coat their bodies with lotions saturated with chemicals. When Spring arrives they are quick to spray their lawn with more chemicals. In Summer they coat their skin with suntan lotions out of fear the sun will give them skin cancer. In reality the chemicals lurking in sunscreens and suntan lotions are causing the cancer.

If sick or ill, most people have a cupboard devoted to medicine which they label as the *medicine cabinet*. These pills and *medicines* are simply concoctions of more chemicals. This is the reality of our modern society. We are a chemical-nation. Sadly, cancer, depression and an array of other illnesses are closely associated with chemical exposure. For the standard citizen, being aware of the chemical exposure from drinking, eating and maintaining normal hygiene is uncommon. These chemicals sedate them, make them more passive and contribute to depression and other health conditions.

In the December 2013 issue of *Reproductive Toxicology*, a study *(35)* was published. After extensive research into what manufacturers add to our food, researchers discovered *about one-thousand additives are in the food supply without the FDA's knowledge. For the eight-thousand additives that the FDA approves, fewer than thirty-eight percent of them have a published feeding study – comprising the basic toxicology test. For direct additives added intentionally to food, only 21.6 percent of the almost four-thousand additives have undergone the feeding studies necessary for scientists to estimate a safe level of exposure. The FDA databases contain reproductive or developmental toxicity data for only 6.7 percent.* A highlight of the findings signifies, *In practice, almost eighty percent of chemical additives being intentionally added to the food supply lack the relevant information needed to estimate the amount that consumers can safely eat in the FDA's own database, and that ninety-three percent lack reproductive or developmental toxicity data – although the FDA requires feeding toxicology data for these chemicals.* To put this in layman's terms, food chemicals are dangerous.

The website, *foodkills.org*, explains that *there are over fourteen-thousand man-made chemicals added to the American food supply today.* If you are buying fresh organic produce and preparing meals at home you are minimizing your overall exposure to these chemicals lurking in food products. A study published in the July 2014 journal *Environmental Research (36)* found that *eating an organic diet for a week can decrease pesticide levels, especially of organophosphates, by up to ninety percent in adults.* These phosphates are linked to many cancers and chronic conditions. During pregnancy, organophosphates are known to penetrate amniotic fluid and are then passed to the infant, leading to childhood cancers.

The best way to avoid these chemicals, as this study clearly shows us, is to eat organic and avoid conventional, processed foods. To cleanse internally we are required to free the body of toxins. This mandates us to temporarily eliminate comfort foods.

For this cleanse to be administered effectively, we are expected to avoid the following items:

- Refined sugars and any artificial, chemical sweeteners. This includes corn syrup, high-fructose corn syrup, sugar, aspartame, amino sweet, glucose syrup, Splenda, and any other type of refined sweetener. The only sweetness in our lives should come from fruits, our significant others, and keeping our children happy.
- Partially-hydrogenated or hydrogenated oils and trans-fatty oils. Any type of oil cooked at a high temperature, including in sauteed foods, becomes trans-fatty, even extra virgin olive oil. One of the most common myths is that cooking with olive oil is the most beneficial to our health, however when you cook these oils over 150 degrees Fahrenheit they become rancid and equivalent to trans-fats. My best advice is not to use any oils, cooked or raw, with the exception of organic virgin unrefined coconut oil used sparingly.
- Monosodium glutamate (MSG), sodium benzoate, other harmful preservatives, and chemical flavor enhancers. These are also referred to as enhanced flavoring agents and they are so poisonous they can be deadly in high doses.
- Food coloring and artificial dyes.
- Bleached flours and refined flours.
- All types of meat, be it mammal, bird, fish, reptile, or amphibian. When heated, meat produces carcinogenic chemicals known as heterocyclic amines and polycyclic aromatic hydrocarbons.
- Dairy products including whey, casein, ice cream, creamer, yogurt, butter, milk, or cheese. These items are often contaminated with the recombinant bovine growth hormone (rBGH).

- Eggs and egg products. In addition to heterocyclic amines, eggs contain arachadonic acid and the mammalian molecule Neu5Gc.
- Sodas and colas. They are loaded with coloring agents, genetically-modified sweeteners, and phosphoric acid.

When you choose to eat processed or animal-based foods as listed above, you degrade health and set a pace towards illness – even if symptoms do not show for years. When taking into consideration they are also patterns that can be difficult to break, eating sugary, salty, oily and fast and junk foods can safely be labeled as addictions. When you eat these things you are not providing your body nutrients, you are nurturing addictions. You feed unwanted microorganisms. Just as cocaine, heroin and prescription drugs alter body chemistry and brain function, so do toxic foods. By upgrading our diet, we find that our health also improves. We become much happier, and gradually shift to a healthier overall lifestyle. To successfully cleanse unwanted emotions we have to eliminate these foods for at least ninety days.

When our diet is lacking nutrients and we ingest chemicals in the form of acrylamides, alcohol, cigarettes, drugs, glycotoxins, industrial toxins and synthetic food additives we compromise our system. This results in toxemia. The blood becomes sticky and accumulates other toxins. Undigested foods ferment and decay into terrain for harmful bacteria. All of this shifts the body pH from alkaline to more acidic. This is a good explanation for how internal cleansing procedures are beneficial. The fermented and decayed foods are eliminated, toxins are expelled, and alkalinity is restored.

In addition to eating organic to avoid food chemicals and pesticide residues, be sure to avoid alcohol, chemical cleaners, cigarettes, fluoridated and chlorinated water, most *beauty* products, a large percentage of cosmetics, lawn chemicals, psychotropic drugs, and suncare products not labeled as organic. If you are unsure of whether or not your health care, hygiene and other *beauty* products and cleaners are safe, access the website of the *Environmental Working Group* (*ewg.org*). On the site you can type in the product you regularly use and the organization

Jacoby

will present you with a grade for how safe the item is. You might be surprised when you search *FeBreze* – which contains ammonium and silicon compounds of high concern. A listed ingredient on the labeling of this product is *quality control ingredients*. After researching further we find that quality control ingredients consist of up to eighty-four different chemicals that are each potentially harmful and known to trigger respiratory disease. If you have an air *freshener* in your home, be sure you remove this product. These contraptions are spraying chemicals at you that may very well be triggering your depressive symptoms. Switch to using essential oil diffusers. Most common air fresheners, bathroom and kitchen cleaners, colognes, conditioners, deodorants, lotions, mouthwashes, perfumes, shampoos, shaving lotions, soaps, sun care products and toothpastes are not safe. Look out for dangerous additives such as parabens, pthalates, and sulfates.

If you are looking for a decent toothpaste, try *Dr. Bronner's*. If you have bad breath, try chewing on mint leaves or an alternate fresh herb. For deodorant the best choice is a clean internal environment. If this is not working, try an organic essential oil or use E.O. Deodorant spray. You can also use essential oils as natural perfumes. Dr. Bronner's soap varieties are an excellent choice for hand soaps and can also be used as body wash. Organic unrefined coconut oil is the best skin moisturizer. If you do not like coconut, try organic raw cacao butter. I use coconut oil on my skin to replace sunscreen, although I carefully moderate how long I spend in direct sunlight. You can also use coconut oil as a mouthwash by *oil pulling*. This is an Ayurvedic healing technique that draws toxins and bacteria out of the gums while cleansing the mouth. *Just Natural* sells a healthy variety of organic shampoos and conditioners. When cleaning your bathroom or kitchen try diluting some organic vinegar in water and simply applying this to surfaces. Vinegar is a highly effective cleaning agent, more powerful than any chemical. After all, dousing something with toxic chemicals is not exactly *cleaning*.

According to the *Environmental Working Group,* in April 2014 the EPA official responsible for reviewing the safety of chemicals used in commercial products was asked *how many chemicals in use are so dangerous they should get a harder look by the agency to protect public health and the environment.* This EPA official who was responsible for reviewing the safety of chemicals that have been linked to everything from cancer to reproductive problems, told lawmakers that *about one thousand chemicals currently found in everyday products need to be reviewed (37).* This news alone should be enough for us to question the safety of everyday products we currently use.

Now that we know what chemicals we should be avoiding, we can discard of the health-damaging food products, household cleaners, and health care products that contain these toxins. Once our living environment is free from these health hazards, we can focus on cleansing our organs to be sure our internal environment is also waste-free.

I encourage you to be mindful of the chemicals you are using. Even going to a car wash requires the use of several chemicals that are toxic to the environment. When we adapt this mindfulness and elevate our awareness of how we are contributing to lowering Earth's frequency, we start to raise our individual radiant frequency. We must step away from being imprisoned to disease and poor health by profitable industries and reach the height of human potentiality. We need to expand consciousness. Let your organs function without being backed up with animal-based foods. Give your skin consent to breathe. Free your home from artificial fragrances. Cleanse your body with wholesome ingredients. Allow your skin to feel the rays of the sun without sunblock. Permit your eyes to feel sunlight without shades.

"Wisdom comes only when you stop searching, and start living the life Creator intended for you." – Hopi Proverb

Heliotherapy – Healing Power of Sunlight

Everything on Earth is nourished by the sun. The food we ingest was converted from light emanating out of this star. Most religions in some way are centered around this source of energy. In Zeitgeist (38) we learn that *history is abundant with carvings and writings reflective of people's respect and adoration for the sun. Cultures have always understood that the sun is responsible for the flourishing of crops and survival of life on this planet. The sun has always been the most adored object of all time.*

The cross of the Zodiac reflects the sun passing through the twelve major constellations over the course of the year. This also mirrors the twelve months of the year, four seasons, and equinoxes and solstices. The twelve constellations have always personified people or animals. The information presented in this film suggests that *the twelve constellations have been represented as places of travel for God's Sun since ten thousand B.C.E. and were identified by names – usually representing elements of nature that happened during that period of time.*

Christianity was devised from the story of Horus. Horus was born on December twenty-fifth and conceived by the virgin Isis-Meri. According to his legacy, *the birth was accompanied by a star in the East and three kings followed this star to locate and adorn him as a newborn savior. At the age of twelve he was a prodigal child teacher. By the age of thirty he was baptized and began his ministry. Horus was known to have had twelve disciples who he traveled with, performing miracles such as healing sick and decrepit people and walking on water. Horus was also referred to as The Truth, The Light, God's Annointed Son, The Good Shepherd, and The Lamb of God. After being betrayed by Typhon, Horus was crucified, buried for three days and then resurrected.*

With the teachings of Christianity we see many similarities. Jesus Christ was conceived by the virgin Mary on December twenty-fifth in Bethlehem. His birth was also associated with a star in the East which three kings followed to locate and adorn him as the new savior. He was a child teacher at twelve, and at the age of thirty was also baptized, beginning his ministry. Jesus had twelve disciples which he traveled about with performing similar miracles. He was also known as the King of Kings, Son of God, Light of the World, Alpha and Omega and Lamb of God. After being betrayed by his disciple, Judas, he was crucified and placed in a tomb. After three days he resurrected and ascended into Heaven. The parallels reveal something far greater than what we presently understand.

Zeitgeist explains further how *this birth sequence is astrological. The star in the east is representative of Sirius, the brightest star in the night sky. On December twenty-fourth, Sirius aligns with the three brightest stars in Orion's Belt. These stars are referred to today as The Three Kings. The Three Kings and the brightest star, Sirius, all point to the place of the sunrise on December twenty-fifth. This is why the Three Kings are said to have followed the star in the east in order to locate the sunrise – reflective of the birth of the sun.*

The winter solstice also occurs around this date in December. *From the summer solstice to winter solstice temperatures drop and days shorten. From the perspective of the northern hemisphere, the sun appears to move south and get smaller and more scarce. The shortening of days and expiration of crops when approaching the winter solstice symbolized the process of death to the ancients. This was the death of the Sun.*

By December twenty-second, the sun reaches her lowest point in the sky and stops moving south for three days. *During this retreat of movement this powerful star rests in the vicinity of the Southern Cross constellation. After this time, on* December twenty-fifth, the Sun moves one degree north, leading to longer days, warmth and Spring. *This translates to the Sun dying on the cross, being dead for three days and then resurrecting. This is why Jesus and numerous other Sun Gods share the crucifixion, three day death, and resurrection concept. This reflects the Sun's transition period before shifting back into the Northern Hemisphere, bringing Spring and salvation.* The resurrection of the Sun was not celebrated until the spring equinox, or Easter, when the star officially emerges over darkness. This is when daytime becomes longer in duration than night.

In this film we also learn that the most obvious of all the astrological symbolism around Jesus regards the twelve disciples. *These simply represent the twelve constellations of the Zodiac, which Jesus – being the Sun – travels about with.* Most religions share similar concepts. We worship the powerful Sun, which brings abundance, life and prosperity to all beings and species.

Mankind today has grown estranged from worshiping this entity. We are plagued with lies and wicked ideologies that lead us to believe the Sun is harmful and we treat the very essence of life as an enemy. People coat their bodies with harmful sunscreens that cause skin cancer and other ailments, wear sunglasses that take away their vision, and even spray metal oxides from jets into the atmosphere to block the Sun's rays from reaching Earth's surface. This confusion enables disharmony and sickness.

Chemicals that lurk in suncare products are known to seep into our blood, stagnate lymph fluid and cause skin cancers and various other unnatural symptoms. When we sungaze in moderation, without harmful sunglasses covering our eyes, we take in life force energy from this star. Light beams emanating from the Sun enhance our vision and revitalize and empower us. Today we are experiencing what is known as global dimming as a result of the pollutants from animal agriculture and dangerous chemicals being emitted into the atmosphere and environment. Earth's surface only receives a fraction of the rays from the sun as she was gifted with a few decades ago. This dissolvement of sunlight is tragic to all species and disconnects us from spirit.

In the early 1900s a Swiss doctor named Auguste Rollier championed the term heliotherapy – or sunlight therapy. He devised a protocol for his patients to sunbathe for health. He successfully healed thousands of patients from arthritis, lupus, nerve damage and tuberculosis by guiding them through sessions of bathing in direct sunlight. Today we could likely see similar success with healing society from what ails us by exposing our flaws and wounds to direct sunlight in moderation. We need the sun to shine at full force if we want to generate goodness globally. In addition, we need to receive biophotons from sun energy in the organic fruits and vegetables we ingest.

One Day

One day, our world will unite.

People of all shapes and sizes, from far away lands and new horizons, will find ways to get along and live alike.

Religious preference will not matter. Wars will cease to exist. There will be cultural vastness and ethnic diversity. Separation will be a fading memory of past mistakes.

We will all believe in who we are, as we stand for our purpose.

Egos will lay themselves down to the principle, we all are not simply created equal, but we must abide by this common ground. We will live this way every day as we build each other up by being kind to other people.

We will understand each other not by the language we speak, but through the language of love. The world will resurrect from this peaceful belief and Earth will be freedom's retreat.

One day we will reconnect with loved ones we have lost. We will be together again and bring out the best in each other. Our vows will stand strong to never again be laid to rest.

We will manifest the peace we are seeking. The life we desire will summon us to seize what we are after. What we work toward will align with conservation of the planet, coexisting with all sentient beings.

We will learn how to smile authentically, stemming from internal happiness, rooted in purity and outpouring from the state of being love.

One day the children of the world will be safe – no matter their upbringing, background, circumstances or which region they live. Each child will have food on their plate. Poverty will not exist. Mothers will not use drugs. Daughters will know where their fathers can be found. The family tree will never fall down. Love will culminate the world around. Laughter and soft-spoken words of peace will be – to all of us – the most fulfilling sounds.

We will beat neglect and abuse to the ground and give our youth the attention they deserve on this united Earth where everyone is equal.

We will provide plant medicines from Gaia to generate love from our soul that uplifts and heals others. We accept that in harmony we can all live an infinite amount of years.

There will be no tears falling from depression, only cheers, as we profess our adoration for individuality, diversity and those we love – recognizing passion as a source to keep our spirits dancing.

One day, we will all live without fear. We will have the choice to honor our dignity, rather than forcing careers.

One day we will all live in beautiful homes constructed from renewable resources, powered by the sun and finding comfort from free energy.

Propane will not be the source for our heat. Our vehicles will be petroleum free. Anger and greed will no longer be the most common diseases.

We will discover our own gold, deep from the mines of our minds, and finally stop exploiting distant lands for raw materials we really do not need.

One day the rainforests will thrive and exotic creatures, indigenous clans and celestial bird tribes will be free from land grabs by corporations. Palm trees will be at peace and orangutan and Sumatran tiger numbers will rise. The frequency of the galaxy will hit an all time high.

We will all be happy through each of life's storms.

We will all feel reborn.

One day the value of life will be more.

Origin of Sickness

We are failing to connect diseases and impurities affecting our air, crops, soil and water with the degeneration of man. Our understanding of sickness does not adhere to the actuality of what plagues mankind. The ailments distressing humanity are symptoms of cultural conditioning, excess, and mind poisoning wherein the mind has been modified to believe in customs, ideologies and traditions that should never be.

Sickness starts the moment a child is taught that eating meat is okay and animals are food. This malady transpires when kids are indoctrinated with the belief that trees should be cut down or that logging and clear-cutting forests is okay. Debilitation is rooted in the idea that chemicals are necessary for cleanliness or agricultural practices.

The origin of disease is mixed in cocktails with heavy metals and viruses and then inoculated in humans with the belief that immunity can somehow be improved by stimulating an underdeveloped immune system with shots. There is an injunction in our path to well-being misleading the masses into thinking our creator made a blunder when developing the human body and that we must depend on chemists to fix the mistake – forcing our way back to health with chemicals. Injecting this poison into the body is not of any benefit to the organism being sickened or for the greater good of humanity.

Infirmities are activated when people believe they can take pills that are composed of a mixture of different poisons to heal themselves from conditions generated from other poisons. They want a quick fix from the sad reality they create for themselves. They want to sin and ingest forgiveness in pill form, delusional from fact, and unaware this is not possible.

Decrepitude begins in the mind when we start abiding by what industries and corporations work so diligently to strategize as the basis of our belief system. This is the formation of a lack of introspect and good will. So sickness is taught in the schools and is broadcast all over the news. We see tidbits of what causes illness advertised in newspapers, on television sets, and on radios and billboards.

Most health conditions can be associated with gut imbalances, or what is referred to as dysbiosis. When we ingest dead foods derived from animals, processed foods, drugs and alcohol, cosmetics on the skin, and prescription pills and injections, this devastates gut health and weakens immunity. Fallacious dietary patterns are so pervasive, and people are so aloof to what is important, that we now have men and women who are disconnected from Mother Earth running congress and dictating the economy. CEO's, lackadaisical consumers, and politicians are responsible for depletion of resources all over the globe. They perpetually impoverish the planet for more things not needed to somehow curb the appetite of inappeasable greed.

Acquiring illness is ubiquitous because microbes on the planet that are harmful have misappropriated humans through chemicals and harmful foods. As people ingest these poisons and become disenchanted, parasites infiltrate their microbiome and take over their brain – warping potentiality. Native Americans refer to this disease of the soul as *Wetiko* (39) – a parasitic spirit who embodies excess and greed and can possess human beings. The Wetiko was once human, but allowed greed and selfishness to transform him into a predatory monster. Now this microbial consciousness preys on other humans who have indulged in excess. Those possessed by Wetiko consume life force from others.

Sickness that burdens society can be reversed once we recondition our mind with fresh perspective. When we accept that our beguiling lifestyle habits impact our health, exclusive of genetics, this warrants us to make changes that prevent and reverse degenerative health conditions. When we clean up our lifestyle, harmful parasites and microbes are cleansed from the body, the colon is flushed, and the microbiome is rebalanced. This frees us to take on consciousness from goodness, nature and Earth. We need to shift away from strengthening the pharmaceutical empire and aiding their profitable agenda by reclaiming ownership of our health.

Hijacking Health – The Medical Trap

When people use drugs – especially pharmaceutical pills – the ecosystem of the gut is altered. As overall health of the microbiome is destabilized, acquisition of illness becomes inevitable. Without a healthy population of gut bacteria, the immune system is vulnerable to penetration by exogenous substances. The business model of the medical establishment uses this as a platform for generating profits. By studying the pharmacokinetics of pharmaceuticals, we learn that compounds in pills require certain enzymes in order to be metabolized from the system. Some important enzymes needed for detoxification are catalase, cytochrome P450, and superoxide dismutase. Fluoride, glyphosate, mercury and several of the chemicals added to municipal water, pesticides, processed foods, prescription pills, and vaccines are known to block and inhibit production of these enzymes. When we experience symptoms of sickness, our discomfort is connected with enzyme responses in the body. Medications are designed to activate certain enzymes while inhibiting others from being synthesized. This enacts the ability to alleviate one symptom while being responsible for generating the next. This is why advertisements for pharmaceutical drugs display warnings of severe harmful side effects associated with each medication. The system is manipulated to remove one symptom and create the next. This keeps a free-flow of revenue streaming.

In 2015 there were 1.1 million doctors of medicine in the United States earning average salaries of $294,000. This equates to over three-hundred billion dollars in salary. There were over four billion retail prescriptions filled in the United States in 2018, and a 2017 *Consumers Reports* study (40) found that fifty-five percent of Americans regularly take prescription medicine. As more prescriptions are filled, the plague of sickness devouring humanity amplifies. We cannot continue ingesting these harmful pills if we wish to experience a health transformation. The medical establishment makes money from people who keep coming back. They are not here to help us revive health or extend longevity.

According to the United States *Government Accountability Office*, pharmaceutical sales revenue increased from $554 billion to $775 billion annually between 2006 and 2015 (41). Research spending on drugs increased from eighty-two billion dollars in 2008 to eighty-nine billion in 2014. As research improves, profits also rise, and the sickness epidemic surges. This clarifies how research being conducted is not executed in search of cures. Research spending goes toward learning ways to prolong disease, exacerbate symptoms, and manage patients for profits until they are no longer of value to the system. Total revenue of the global pharmaceutical market exceeds one trillion dollars – with forty-five percent going to businesses in the United States. This equates to a lot of sick people, especially in the country considered to be the most prosperous nation. The major exports and cash commodities from the United States are chemicals and pharmaceutical drugs. This is a drug-dealing nation slanging poisons for profit.

Afghanistan is the largest producer of opium in the world, and opium is needed for much of the drugs used to manage pain. When the United States invaded Afghanistan in 2001, opium poppies were grown on around seventy-four thousand hectares of land (42). Since that time the government has spent over one-million dollars a day, or nine billion total dollars, on *counter narcotics* in this region. Sixteen years later, in 2017, opium production increased and was grown on over three-hundred and twenty-eight thousand hectares. Bearing of opium elevated over four-fold. This leads us to wonder where this money is truly going. An opioid epidemic has also transpired in the United States since the invasion of Afghanistan. More people are addicted to, and dependent on opioids than ever before in history. The *American Academy of Pain Medicine* claims nearly one-third of all Americans report they are suffering from chronic pain. Profits from pain management exceed twenty-four billion dollars annually in the United States alone. Not only is the medical industry fueling the opium war in Afghanistan, this outfit also propels the petroleum industry.

In 1897, German chemist Felix Hoffman synthesized acetylsalicylic acid (Aspirin) from compounds in petroleum. This provoked John D. Rockefeller, founder of *Standard Oil Trust*, to fund research for discovering more chemicals from the oil he managed. Petroleum is refined and separated into chemical reagents used to make pesticides, pharmaceuticals, and plastics. Most medical devices today are assembled using petroleum products and many pharmaceutical pills contain derivatives of petroleum. In a 2001 publication *(43)*, we learn that benzene, cumene, phenol and other petrochemical aromatics constitute the formulas used for manufacturing Aspirin, Penicillin and many drugs used for cancer treatments. Polymers from petroleum are used to make pill capsules and coatings. Time-release drugs rely on a tartaric acid-based polymer that slowly dissolves to administer controlled doses of medication. Even drug packaging is made using plastics. Today the medical industry is built on a petroleum foundation.

The medical establishment takes advantage of anyone who buys into their system. This industry exists solely because people are sick. Without sickness the empire would collapse. This is why they will never provide cures or assist us in strengthening our immunity. This also deciphers why medical doctors are limited in nutritional education and taught to misinform patients about the importance of diet. They need us to continue eating low-quality foods so we depend on health-depleting drugs that suffice their income. Similar to how companies hire salesmen to promote and sell their products, the medical establishment hires doctors. In the same fashion that these salesmen are trained to believe solely and passionately in this product, doctors are trained to believe in the non-existing benefits of pills and prescriptions.

We need to acknowledge how powerful our immune system can be when we alienate ourselves from this harmful *pill for every ill* paradigm and embrace purity. If we nourish our body, mind, and soul with potent elements from nature, we resurrect good health. By abstaining from ingesting carcinogens, we are freed from cancer and disease.

Manufacturing Cancer

When the *American Cancer Society* was founded in 1913, there were an estimated seventy-five thousand people living with cancer in the United States (44). After the *National Cancer Act of 1971*, America declared a war on cancer. According to the *CDC*, there were about three million people living with cancer that year. Thirty years later, in 2001, this number tripled to nine million. Almost fifty years after the war on cancer initiative was launched, there were over eighteen million new cases of cancer reported globally in 2018, and nine million cancer deaths (45). In this span of time, trillions of dollars have been invested in cancer research, only to see prevalence of cancer and disease higher than ever.

The United States government provides funding for an average of up to five billion dollars a year on cancer research (46). Spending on cancer medicines is projected to exceed one-hundred fifty billion dollars by 2020. Annual medical costs of cancer care are expected to reach 173 billion dollars by the year 2020. Close to seven billion dollars of tax-payer funds are designated to cancer research through various federal agencies. This money is not invested in finding cures. Proceeds from donations go toward discovering new drugs to *treat* cancer, and researching how cancers can be developed with chemicals. The aim is to devise strategies for prolonging cancer treatments and managing finances of victims.

This year there are just over twenty-thousand active oncologists in the United States earning salaries close to a half-million dollars. This calculates to nearly ten billion dollars a year in salary going to oncologists alone. Global spending on cancer medicines increased from 96 billion dollars in 2013 to 133 billion in 2017. People think they are dying from cancer, yet are truly perishing from the negligence of oncologists, incompetence of doctors, fraudulent research institutes, poor lifestyle habits, ingestion of animal fats and proteins, and believing in the lies that construct Western society.

Conventional methods of fighting cancer have a three-percent overall cure rate. Oncologists have no coherence of what causes the development of cancer in the body, and they also lack any competence of knowing how to heal this condition. Doctors are trained to diagnose disorders, manage symptoms, and prescribe pills that are constituted of a mixture of poisons known to inhibit enzyme production and weaken detoxification pathways. Oncologists use chemotherapy drugs, radiation treatments and surgeries in attempts to fight cancer. The goal is to prolong cancerous conditions in the body and manage symptoms until patients are sucked dry of their money. Once drained of their finances, and after their estates have been repossessed through reverse mortgages, they perish through a combination of chemotherapy, radiation poisoning, and lethal injection of morphine.

Lifestyle habits acquired through manufactured culture are estranged from the habits that would be adapted in a natural environment. Meat, dairy, and eggs ravage healthy organs and cellular functions. Cancer is a direct result of absorbing the dishonesty that constructs Western culture. The lies we inhale in smokes. The deception in each alcoholic drink. The wine from grapevines that pollute much of Northern California. The murder in meat. The theft in dairy. The nutritional confusion enshrining the egg. This all feeds the cancerous plague.

Cancer is an after-effect of soul poisoning. A symptom of being alienated from your intrinsic nature. When our culture is invalid, diet is inadequate, and lifestyle is disharmonious, cancer makes a home from your cells and tissues. One of the greatest threats to our livelihood is injections from syringes. When cocktails are injected deep into our interstitium, they remain for a long duration of time. The various toxins slowly release into cerebrospinal, lymphatic, and interstitial fluids. As the compounds injected move from the tissues into the blood, this results in an onslaught of symptoms reflective of serious illness. Formation of malignant tumors are triggered by the compaction of attenuated viruses, heavy metals, and the nagalase enzyme entering the body in an unnatural way through vaccinations.

Injecting Deformity, Destroying Immunity

Imagine if we diverted all of the energy that is wasted trying to create hysteria around whether or not people choose to vaccinate, and instead dedicated this same passion toward getting to the root of health problems. What if mainstream media and other organizations started raising awareness about the dangers of glyphosate and other poisonous chemicals that contaminate our air, food and water? What if we collectively generated the same amount of energy toward ending pollution, cleaning up our air, food and water, and stopping the root cause of disease?

There is an astonishing frenzy within the mainstream media circus revolving around a fabricated measles crisis. There have been just over seven-hundred reported cases of measles this year (2019) in the United States out of a total population of 327.2 million. This equates to 0.0002151589 percent of people contracting this condition. How is this an epidemic? Contrary to this, one in fifty-nine vaccinated children are developing autism and neurodegenerative disease. This means over five million kids are afflicted with autism that lasts a lifetime, compared to just over seven-hundred with a measles rash that subsides in a week. The United States also has a high infant mortality rate, being 5.8 or 0.58 percent, of every one-thousand children. They are also one of the only countries that vaccinates at birth.

What a lot of people overlook is the fact that these measles outbreaks are not eruptions of strains of the wild measles virus. When flare-ups occur, measles viruses that spread are those that have been attenuated and genetically manufactured in labs specifically for vaccines. The wild version of measles today is pretty much non-existent. The only reason why the measles virus still persists is because they inoculate innocent kids with manufactured strains through syringes. These kids then become carriers of lab-designed measles strains and spread, or shed, this version of measles to others. Vaccinated children are sadly the only carriers of this virus. Be mindful of what the vaccine industry is coercing you into believing.

How could a kid who has never been injected with a lab-made version of a disease, or has no trace of a virus in their system, be responsible for spreading this malady to those who have had the virus injected into their blood stream and tissues? There is no logical argument for why anyone should worry about people who are unvaccinated spreading measles. If the vaccine worked, then there would be no reason to declare an epidemic and scare people into injecting an array of harmful chemicals into their kids. If you have not had the attenuated virus injected into your system, then there is no way you could ever spread the virus.

Measles is a mild rash that goes away in days. This is not something to panic about. Being exposed to this rash naturally is way different than having a virus cocktail directly injected into your blood, tissues, and interstitial fluid. Neurological disorders and the devastation of immunity that result from the injections of aluminum, formaldehyde, glyphosate, thimerosal, and other harmful ingredients in vaccines are often permanent, almost always debilitating, and even cause death. Each of these compounds inhibit our ability to produce CYP450 enzymes, which are responsible for detoxifying heavy metals and poisons. They also block the antioxidant glutathione from being manufactured in the body. Without glutathione we cannot protect cells from the damage caused by free radicals and heavy metals.

The current vaccine schedule requires children to be ambushed with forty-six different shots by the time they are eighteen years old. Never once has the full schedule been tested for safety or efficacy. Few of the vaccines have had brief safety tests, but never the entire schedule altogether. Today's children are the control subject undergoing a dangerous experiment.

If you like vaccines, get your shots. Please use common sense though, and try your best not to ridicule and generate hate toward those with a different perspective. Be mindful of hidden agendas. Why would the medical industry, which only exists because people are sick, want so badly to prevent people from getting sick? That would be a horrible business model. The vaccine industry is a multi-billion dollar industry that profits from inoculating children with chemicals and viruses.

There is no evidence of a vaccine ever saving a life, yet doctors and pediatricians continue to regurgitate the same propaganda: *Vaccines have saved thousands of lives.* Vaccines are not designed to save lives. The concept of artificial immunization was established in an attempt to prevent disease. If someone was on their deathbed close to dying and miraculously recovered after being administered a vaccine, this would be an example of a vaccine saving a life. Unfortunately a vaccination saving a life is impossible, although the thought is nice.

The only way to test the safety of vaccines or determine whether or not they cause neurodegenerative disorders would be to test vaccinated versus unvaccinated children. The industry refuses to fund these studies. Several independent studies exist however, and the results overwhelmingly support the notion that unvaccinated children are far healthier. This has nothing to do with so-called *herd immunity*. This has everything to do with a child being much healthier and safer when they are not injected with an onslaught of chemicals, heavy metals, and viruses in dangerous cocktails before their immune system has developed.

The results of the first peer-reviewed study comparing vaccinated versus unvaccinated children was published briefly in February 2017 and then banned from the journal *Frontiers In Pediatrics*. The study, *Vaccination and Health Outcomes: A Survey of Six to Twelve-Year old Vaccinated and Unvaccinated Children based on Mothers' Reports (47)*, analyzed 666 children of which 261 were unvaccinated. Vaccinated children were found to be *significantly more likely than the unvaccinated to have been diagnosed with a neurodevelopmental disorder.* Risk of developing Autism Spectrum Disorder (ASD) was *4.7 fold higher in vaccinated children.* ADHD symptoms also rose *4.7 fold higher* and learning disability risk was *3.7 fold higher.* Overall the *vaccinated children in the study were 3.7 times more likely to have been diagnosed with some kind of neurodevelopmental disorder.* Vaccinated children were also significantly more likely *to be diagnosed with an immune-related disorder.* Risk of allergic rhinitis was *over thirty times higher in vaccinated children* while risk of other allergies was *increased 3.9 fold* and eczema risk was *increased 2.4 fold. Unvaccinated children were also less likely to suffer from ear infections and pneumonia. Vaccinated children had 3.8 times greater odds of a middle ear infection and 5.9 times greater odds of a bout with pneumonia.* This study demonstrates clearly how inoculating children with attenuated viruses through vaccines, when their immune system and brain are both significantly undeveloped, damages immunity and alters neurodevelopmental growth.

Many people blindly support this industry and claim vaccines are safe without knowing how dangerous, fraudulent and ineffective vaccines truly are. They refuse to acknowledge the overwhelming evidence exposing vaccines as unsafe, and regurgitate propaganda compiled by vaccine manufacturers ruling vaccines as risk-free. Why would they care so much about whether or not others vaccinate their kids? If vaccines truly worked, a vaccinated child would have no chance of catching a disease they are vaccinated against. If an unvaccinated child were to develop illness, this would simply result in another customer for the medical establishment. While vaccine proponents are quick to claim children who are not vaccinated will spread disease, or that viruses mutate, the opposite holds to be true. Vaccinated children are the ones carrying diseases. Several childhood vaccines contain live viruses that are not attenuated and once in the system they can spread the diseases to other children who have not been injected. All vaccine inserts even declare that there are many harmful side effects from each vaccine. Take time to read them.

The detrimental effects of vaccines are associated with aluminum and thimerosal adjuvants, formaldehyde, polysorbate 80, and other chemicals added to the vaccine cocktails. What may be of gravest danger though, is an enzyme known as nagalase enzyme. The human body uses a protein known as GcMAF (Globulin-component Macrophage Activating Factor) to effectively eradicate diseases and viruses from the body. This protein is made and released into the blood by T and B lymphocytes when the Vitamin-D binding protein (DBP) combines with the Gc protein. GcMAF is considered by many to be the single most effective compound for killing cancer cells and is also effective for reversing autism and even HIV. When nagalase (N-acetylgalactosaminidase) enzyme enters the human body, Gc protein is no longer able to bind with DBP protein. This results in formation of GcMAF being inhibited. The nagalase enzyme (48) therefore compromises immunity, causing immunodeficiency syndrome as well as neurodegenerative disorders. This enzyme can be defined as *an extracellular matrix-degrading enzyme secreted by cancerous cells in the process of tumor invasion*. Nagalase is also a component of the envelope protein of various virions such as HIV and influenza.

An interesting fact about nagalase is that this enzyme is found in high concentrations in autistic children, yet not present in children at birth. The enzyme only becomes present after vaccination. This enzyme is secreted by cancerous cells and viruses, especially attenuated viruses immersed in vaccine cocktails. When contents of an immunization shot are injected into the blood of any mammal, the victim is inoculated with unknown amounts of nagalase enzyme. Once in the body, this enzyme blocks the body's ability to produce GcMAF and macrophages of the immune system can no longer use this protein to fight off cancerous cells, infections, or viruses.

Before the mysterious death of Dr. Jeffrey Bradstreet, he successfully treated eleven-hundred patients with various health issues using administration of GcMAF and had an eighty-five percent success rate. Fifteen percent of the autistic subjects he worked with were completely reversed of their autism. Since 1990, fifty-nine research papers have been published on the healing effects of GcMAF. Of these, perhaps the most important are those conducted by Nubuto Yamamoto (49).

A common mistake made by vaccine advocates is bringing up diseases from decades ago, or even over a century ago. These people still live in fear over something they know nothing about. They stand firm behind the belief vaccines were responsible for eradicating smallpox and polio. They fail to mention, or notice, that the polio virus had already declined ninety-nine percent before the vaccine was introduced. Polio-like symptoms occurred after the introduction of the harmful pesticide known as DDT. When DDT was banned, the symptoms labeled as polio gradually declined. Polio was never a virus, and there has never been any strain of a virus ever extracted from a patient who was diagnosed as having polio. Smallpox was a livestock disease that originated from humans drinking milk from infected udders of cows. The process of pasteurizing cows milk, coupled with the introduction of plumbing to cities, led to the eventual decline and eradication of smallpox. Never was a vaccine ever responsible for reducing or eliminating any diseases of the past. This is all a hoax used to sell the public on the belief that injecting poison into their blood can somehow help them, when in reality this is creating lifelong customers for the medical industry. The concept of artificial immunization has generated billions of dollars for this industry.

A study in the November 2016 *Science* journal, *Potent Protection Against H5N1 and H7N9 Influenza Via Childhood Hemagglutinin Imprinting (50)*, shows how exposure to natural influenza viruses in young children can provide lifelong immunity to that particular strain when the body is permitted to fight off the invasion naturally. The results indicate that *an individual's first influenza A virus infection confers lifelong protection against severe disease from novel hemagglutinin (HA) subtypes in the same phylogenetic group*. As researchers analyzed further they determined that protective HA imprinting is the crucial explanatory factor, and this provides up to seventy-five percent protection against severe infection and eighty percent protection against death for H5N1 and H7N9 – two deadly strains of influenza. When children are shot up with attenuated influenza strains each year since birth, in accordance with the current vaccine schedule, the ability of the immune system is compromised and sickness becomes inevitable.

A January 2017 Kaiser study published in JAMA Pediatrics, *Association Between Influenza Infection and Vaccination During Pregnancy and Risk of Autism Spectrum Disorder (51)*, analyzed over forty-five thousand women and found an elevated risk of birth defects, in addition to a twenty percent higher risk of autism in children whose mothers received a first-

Jacoby

trimester flu shot. The CDC also discovered women who had flu shots were over seven times more likely to experience a miscarriage.

In 2019, *Children's Health Defense* filed a lawsuit on behalf of *Informed Consent Action Network*, seeking all clinical trial data used by the FDA to approve influenza vaccines for pregnant women. The FDA was unable to provide records of any data. The manufacturers of flu and Tdap vaccines even warn against their use for pregnant mothers in the package inserts, stating that the effects are unknown of what could happen to unborn babies and that there is insufficient data. Even with no testing ever conducted, the CDC has still recommended flu shots for pregnant mothers since 2004 and Tdap shots since 2011. The FDA website states that they have never approved any vaccines specifically for use during pregnancy to protect infants. The CDC even revealed in 2015 that the flu shot can only be up to nineteen percent effective, yet the potential damaging effects can be far more detrimental to health than simply acquiring influenza for a short period of time.

A March 2018 study published in *Journal of Trace Elements in Medicine and Biology, Aluminum In Brain Tissue and Autism (52)*, found that monocytes (white blood cells) in children who are autistic that form at the site of injection from vaccines escort aluminum from the vaccines directly into the brain. Results exhibit that all children studied who were considered autistic had aluminum enter the brain through pro-inflammatory cells that were loaded up with aluminum in the blood or lymphatic fluid. *The majority of aluminum was found within microglia cells and astrocytes. Aluminum was also found in lymphocytes in the meninges and in similar inflammatory cells in the vasculature. There was clear evidence of inflammatory cells heavily loaded with aluminum entering the brain via meningeal membranes and the blood-brain-barrier.*

A 2011 study published in *Current Medical Chemistry, Aluminum Vaccine Adjuvants: Are They Safe? (53)*, questions the acceptance of aluminum adjuvants being considered safe. Throughout all history there have never been any safety studies conducted to determine whether or not the injection of aluminum carries health risks. This particular study points out the scarcity of data on toxicology and pharmacokinetics of aluminum compounds in vaccines. Researchers found that despite the ongoing use of aluminum adjuvants and acceptance of these compounds as being safe, they carry the potential to induce serious immunological disorders in humans. These adjuvants carry risk for autoimmunity, long-term brain inflammation, and neurological complications.

Aluminum is included in vaccines as an adjuvant. This means the aluminum serves a purpose of activating the immune system and signaling an alert that a xenobiotic, or foreign antigen, has been introduced in the body through the vaccine. This foreign molecule, aluminum, is then taken up by immune system cells (macrophages) and transported around the body to various organs, including into the brain. Aluminum adjuvants can cause brain injury and autoimmune diseases. A publication in the Winter 2016 edition of *Journal of American Physicians and Surgeons*, *Aluminum In Childhood Vaccines Is Unsafe (54)*, notes how aluminum is a neurotoxin. The study author explains how children and infants are repeatedly injected with aluminum adjuvants from multiple vaccines during critical periods of brain development. He shares how a child in the 1980's would have only been exposed to 1,250 micrograms of aluminum by the time they are eighteen months, yet with the increase in number of vaccines today that number has risen to 4,925 micrograms.

A November 2004 study published in *Annals of Neurology (55)*, *Neuroglial Activation and Neuroinflammation In the Brain of Patients With Autism*, explains how autistic patients have activated microglia and astroglia cells. Using immuno-cytochemical studies, researchers were able to demonstrate how this activation of microglia and astroglia, along with cytokine profiling, indicated that macrophage chemo-attractant protein (MCP)–1 and tumor growth factor–β1, derived from neuroglia were the most prevalent cytokines in brain tissues. A November 2009 study published in *Journal of Inorganic Biochemistry*, *Aluminum Hydroxide Injections Lead To Motor*

Deficits and Motor-Neuron Degeneration (56), indicates that injected aluminum stimulates activation of a glial inflammatory response in the lumbar cord, and this is noted as a key early stage in the pathological events leading to motor neuron death.

Dr. Paul Patterson introduced epidemiological studies showing how a viral or bacterial infection during pregnancy increases risk for a child to be born with a neurodegenerative disorder such as autism. In his 2006 publication in *Engineering and Science* journal, *Pregnancy, Immunity, Schizophrenia, and Autism (57)*, the concept of *Maternal Immune Activation* is introduced. His research team discovered that activation of a pregnant woman's immune system can alter the growth of cells in the fetal brain. Autism-related symptoms in infants were found to be from the body reacting to the mother's infection, not from the infection itself. When an infant with an underdeveloped immune and neuronal system experiences this counteraction, the reaction triggers the formation of proinflammatory cytokines in the brain. The premature activation of microglial cells mutates natural development of the neuronal system and this leads to encephalitis and cognitive disorders. Of these cytokines, interleukin-6 seems to be most harmful. Activation of the immune system during brain development causes a disruption in immune system signaling. *Aluminum and immune activation are connected, because aluminum triggers immune activation, and interleukin-6 specifically. Aluminum stimulates IL-6 in the brain. Aluminum also stimulates Th2 activation, a type of immune activation shown to impair brain development in animal studies. So the issues of aluminum adjuvant toxicity and immune activation are connected.*

A February 2014 study published in Molecular Psychiatry, *Elevated Maternal C-Reactive Protein and Autism In A National Birth Cohort*, analyzed 1.2 million pregnant women and found that elevations in C-Reactive Protein (CRP) during pregnancy were associated with a forty-three percent increased risk of their child developing autism. A few years prior to this information being released, study results showed an increase in CRP levels in pregnant mothers within two days of receiving a flu vaccine (58).

This publication is titled, *Inflammatory Responses To Trivalent Influenza Virus Vaccine Among Pregnant Women*, and was included in the November 2011 *Vaccine* journal. An additional study published in the January 2017 *JAMA Pediatrics* journal, *Association Between Influenza Infection and Vaccination During Pregnancy and Risk of Autism Spectrum Disorder*, displayed an elevated risk of birth defects and autism in the offspring of mothers who received influenza vaccines during pregnancy (59).

Awareness by vaccine manufacturers of the harmful effects of vaccinating, yet continued support for this malpractice, is a blatant misuse of power. Merck is being sued for fraud, as they allegedly skewed study results to make their mumps vaccine look effective. They released misleading information to the public so people would believe their vaccine is over ninety percent effective. The MMR vaccine was also exposed as being an agent for inducing autism. There are over one-hundred peer-reviewed studies linking vaccines with autism.

How could a perfectly healthy child, who lives an organic lifestyle, is breastfed by his vegan mother, and has never been exposed to any type of disease only be healthy because other kids were injected with heavy metals in his community? Better yet, how could this perfectly healthy child who has no symptoms or traces of disease be responsible for infecting another child who has already been injected with this disease? None of the explanations, *facts*, or points presented by vaccine proponents make sense. Less than half of the adult population is up to date on their vaccines, which expels the myth of herd immunity, so why are they not at risk for these so-called infectious diseases? Should we isolate all vaccinated kids from every adult who is not up-to-date on their artificial immunizations, and escalate panic over adults spreading disease to kids too? Herd immunity is not, never has been, and never will be possible. Herd immunity today can be defined as society being immune to the truth. People are so easily manipulated, and so quick to inject their children because they are fearful of how they will be perceived, that they have disunified from the truth.

When disease break outs occur, close to ninety percent of those who catch the disease are fully up-to-date on their vaccinations for the same disease they are experiencing. When you look at something such as the measles virus, the binding receptor in the human body for this condition was different in the wild version of the virus than with the mutated, lab-grown strain of the virus. Today the virus is spreading because they are inoculating millions of babies with a synthetic version of the disease, and the body is more susceptible because the lab-grown version defies nature and is able to evade the immune system after being genetically altered by medical scientists who need children to be sick in order for them to attain job security.

Why are people even risking the chances of their kids developing autism or neurodegenerative disorders from vaccines when there is a much safer, far more effective way to protect them from disease and boost their immunity? The best method for prevention starts with their mother eating a plant-based, drug-free diet, and breastfeeding them. Once weaned from the breastmilk, the child should never again be exposed to any type of animal-derived foods. There are molecules in dairy, eggs, and meat that are binding receptors for diseases. Veganism could be the safest form of immunization.

The sialic acids known as N-glycolylneuraminic acid (Neu5Gc) and N-acetylneuraminic acid (Neu5Ac) act as binding receptors for several of the infectious diseases children are being vaccinated against. These include infant meningitis, influenza, and pertussis (whooping cough). While the body naturally produces some strains of Neu5Ac, those responsible for binding to pathogens are only derived from animals. In addition, the Neu5Gc molecule only enters the human body after ingesting animal-derived foods such as cheese, eggs, meat and milk. Rather than injecting unidentifiable compounds, harmful heavy metals, the nagalase enzyme, and various other disease-inducing substances into the blood via vaccines, why should we not simply educate parents on the dangers of feeding their kids animal-derived foods?

If you know someone who believes unvaccinated kids are carriers of disease, there are ways to educate them kindly. Try starting with simple questions such as: *Are you implying that children who live in a healthy environment, breastfeed from healthy vegan mothers, and are not exposed to any disease or chemicals carry disease? How can they infect other children who have been intentionally injected with the very disease you fear they may catch to supposedly protect them from the disease?* You could also try asking, *are you suggesting that these children are only healthy because other kids in their community were injected with chemicals and attenuated strains of diseases? Can you explain the logic behind this? If the vaccines worked, and were truly effective, how could a child who does not carry disease spread disease to a child who was already induced with this disease for prevention?* I have already read several attempted explanations asserting mutations of disease are responsible, yet this argument only displays evidence that no vaccine could ever be effective with the ability of viruses to mutate. In fact, this only makes the concept of vaccinating far more dangerous.

If we want to get to the root of what is plaguing our children with neurodegenerative disorders, we need to be more open-minded. We need to question medical authority. As parents, if you have an instinctual feeling that vaccines may not be safe, you need to execute your parental rights and protect your child. Do not be stricken with fear or allow other people to bully you into dissolving your protective instinct. Most importantly, we need to enrich the health of our children through nutritionally adequate foods resonating with the highest radiant frequency.

Always be mindful of profitable agendas. Perform research independently without feeding into propaganda. Remember that the people who are questioning the efficacy and safety of vaccines are almost always parents who have watched their children suffer life-threatening consequences from adverse reactions to these shots. There is a reason why over four billion dollars have been paid out to families of vaccine-injured children. When your child's health and safety is at risk of being compromised, you are her only voice. You are his only armor of protection.

Saving Future Generations

I am concerned for future generations of children. There has never been so much pollution circulating around the world. Our careless acts are stealing the inexplicable beauty from them we need to preserve for their inheritance. I also grieve for kids today. Why should innocent children be exposed to so much anger, confusion and corruption? We need to harmonize more with nature and attune to what truly matters. No profits will ever be more important than clean air, soil and water. Humanity is plundering to sickness and becoming endangered. The children today are sicker than ever before.

Every day, forty-three children are diagnosed with cancer. Twelve percent of them do not survive (60). More than forty-thousand children undergo treatments for cancer each year. Statistics propose that approximately one in two-hundred children in the United States will develop cancer before their twentieth birthday. A child is diagnosed with cancer every three minutes somewhere in the world. Every year there are more than three-hundred thousand kids pronounced as *cancerous*. The *Citizen's Commission on Human Rights* reports that over seven million children aged zero to seventeen are taking psychiatric drugs (61). Over two million of these are anti-depressants. The CDC proudly recognizes over ninety-five percent of all kindergartners as being vaccinated. Concurrently, *Autism Speaks* informs us that one in fifty-nine of these children are diagnosed with autism-spectrum disorder (62). Not only are we failing to protect Earth, we are also insufficiently defending our children.

Over eighteen percent of all children aged two to nineteen are considered obese. This condition affects the lives of close to fourteen million kids. *National Children's Alliance* estimates that nearly seven-hundred thousand boys and girls in the United States are abused annually (63). *American Civil Liberties Union* documents nearly sixty-thousand youth under the age of eighteen are incarcerated in juvenile jails and prisons in the United States. If we cannot provide a safe haven for kids where they are shielded from abuse, chemicals, crime and disease then what are we doing?

When a soul enters the body, that soul either grows or atrophies in relation to lifestyle patterns adapted by the human organism she occupies. When a new soul is born, the energy potentiality of that child is limited. Boundaries become more restrictive as the body is exposed to animal-derived foods, chemicals, fluoride, processed foods, and vaccines. If this child is nourished organically with love, plant-based nutrition, nature, and wisdom, the soul blossoms, matures and ripens within the terrain – thereby expanding. This soulful expansion extends longevity. If this child is subjected to abuse, neglect, and low-quality nourishment, the soul depletes to the point of complete exhaustion and the human organism is depleted.

A child should not experience sickness and is never to be subjected to abuse. Vaccination and ingestion of animal-based and processed foods is as abusive as neglect and abandonment. When a child is infected with various toxins in vaccine cocktails, the xenobiotics are permanently positioned in the interstitial fluid, making them difficult to metabolize. Premature activation of the microglial cells in a child with an underdeveloped immune system creates sickness in the body, stunts neuronal development, weakens immunity, and permanently alters the population of bacteria in the gut.

When a child is sick, this is not a sign of the immune system working, or an indicator that this system is developing as a result of *exposure to this condition*. This is a symptom of poisoning and is as unnatural as extinction of species or deforestation. The child who is not vaccinated, raised in a natural environment on a strictly vegan diet, and breastfeeds from a mother who abstains from ingesting poisons and maintains a healthy vegan diet, will rarely – if ever – experience any sort of illness.

The most severe mental illness that plagues man is this acquired belief that we do not need to take care of our children. When your business dumps chemicals or animal feces into waterways, your kids eventually bathe in and drink this same water. Be mindful of the butterfly effect your actions have on future generations.

Soul Never Dies – Poem For My Brother

I hear your isolated tears falling gently to the dirt. You are a part of the soil now, you climbed your way back into Earth.

Some say you arrived too soon, but I know you had to find a way to heal your wounds.

You left with no fear. Created the only lasting cure. Now you are pure. No more court mandates or medications. You chose your last sedation. You established eternal unification. The train tracks carried you to liberation.

I know your mind was controlled by psychotropic pills. Against your will, forced to consume the poison eating away your soul. Part of a medical experiment you never wanted to join. Your strength to endure nine long years of prescription torture and pain empowered me more than you will ever know.

Maybe you did not mean to leave as soon as you did. Although we wish you had stayed, we all accept your decision as is. The courage you garnered to take on that train was your only escape from the fate of a psychiatrist's negligence.

You are everywhere now. That shooting star, the electric energy could be you. Everywhere I look, in all I see move, I notice traces of your silhouette. Maybe you are walking on the moon. The butterfly emerging from her cocoon. A mysterious flower waiting for the sun to rise so he can bloom.

I feel your rhythm in the blues. I wonder if you visited the Redwoods first, or made your way to the forests in Peru. As sad as I am, I know freedom was waiting for you. Please don't cry no more, you shall be happy. This Western society had you so confused. There is more to life than fitting into a system constructed from abuse.

Now you can dance and the skies will rain. No more pain. You can fly with unbroken wings. No more trouble in your brain. You have found what makes you sane. The solution, always, was to get away.

You are everything now. That bolt of lightning, those drops of rain. The luster on a lion's mane. I feel your energy all around. The sun is now your soul. The roots are your bones. Earth has become your throne. The universe is your home.

I see you walking in the distance. Hear you talking. Feel your presence. You discovered the miracle drug. Learned how to rise above. Your spirit helps me understand what is love.

You are everyone now. I see pieces of you in each who passes by. A part of you glimmers in Nevaeh's light. There is some of your strength in Arlo's might. Your smile never dies. In your eyes there is that look of, oh how I wonder why.

I hear you laughing. Could never forget your voice. Still feel you tremble. I know you had no choice. An angel started a new life. You walk by my side. Teaching me not to be blind. Opening my perspective to see beyond the propaganda and mainstream lies. Leading me out of darkness and into light.

Maybe you are a Messiah in disguise. The magical child within who only wants to be recognized.

Harvesting Mental Illness

My brother was not mentally ill. His afflictions were a result of his environment. No person will ever convince me that his systematic poisoning was genetic or natural. Before a psychiatrist intervened and manipulated my mother into believing he needed pills to dull his intellect, he was bright, radiant, and smart. The psychiatric drugs dimmed his shine. He was victimized by an industry that prescribes drugs to children under the age of five.

The origin of mental illness is rooted in adapting a harmful lifestyle that depletes health. Believing we need to eat dead animals for nourishment, or drink a substance formulated in nature to stimulate the growth of a cow for good health, are symptoms of mental illness. Poisoning ourselves with chemicals and processed foods, and trusting doctors and pills will heal us, is also a symptom of cognitive confusion.

Mental illness transpires when the iris of a young child is affixed to a digital screen. There is no sustenance in environments that lack plants and trees. Television is void of the substance we need to elevate creativity. Neuronal stabilization is displaced with artificiality. Anxiety is not a disorder, but a side-effect of corporate takeover. Technology has induced a weakness of mind in those who have grown estranged from their primitive terrain. Human consciousness has been expropriated by parasites. Man has become familiarized with killing animals for food, drinking alcoholic fools brew, smoking carcinogenic tools, popping poison pills, bathing in water saturated with fluoride, and generations of lies manufactured by profiteers who poison and kill for profits that have no real appeal.

Sickness starts the moment flesh or milk from another species enters the human body. Disease begins to unleash when vaccines are shot into the tissues of infants with underdeveloped immunity. Being ill is inevitable when you ingest pharmaceutical pills. We are not born with mental illness, the environment we are immersed in at birth harbors this condition for us.

The penal system strips prisoners of their inherent right of expression. A criminal mind is transplanted through adulteration of consciousness cultivated by poor lifestyle, erroneous education, and cultural conditioning. The assembly of highly profitable industry is often forged at the expense of human freedom, warped minds, and lifetimes of grief, pain and suffering endured by those exposed to this cruelty.

The reason why addiction and mental illness are so rarely cured in this current paradigm is because mental health professionals target the mind as a culprit, when in reality the gut is the origin for addiction and mental illness. When people use drugs, especially dangerous pharmaceutical pills, they generate parasitic microbes in the gut. This microbial consciousness eventually seizes the human brain. If we wish to heal from these conditions, we must abstain from ingesting or being injected with chemicals, attune to Gaia's frequency, cleanse our bodily systems, and eat diets consisting of zero dead matter and an array of colorful fruits and vegetables.

"We do not need to consume a lot to be happy. With mindfulness, any moment can become a happy moment. Savoring one simple breath, taking a moment to witness the bright blue sky, or fully enjoying the presence of a loved one can be more than enough to make us happy. Each one of us needs to reconnect with ourselves, our loved ones and with Earth. Money, power or consuming is not what assures us happiness. What we need is to have love and understanding in our heart." – Thich Nhat Hanh

A friendly reminder:

All that we love is medicine.

Anything that harms us is a drug.

Take the medicine in efficient doses, as needed, and abstain from the drugs.

We are culturally conditioned to see all of this backwards, as harmful drugs are considered medicine, and too many people abuse these drugs under the impression they will have a medicinal effect. Plants are our only medicine.

Biology of Depression

"The moment you change your perception is the moment you rewrite the chemistry of your body." – Dr. Bruce Lipton, *The Biology of Belief*

My mother was convinced by doctors to give my brother psychotropic pills at thirteen so he could be more attentive in school. This dulling of his vivacity eventually became a gateway for them to introduce him to drugs and pills for depression. The reality of the situation is that my brother possessed a strong spirit that did not want to be conformed to an artificial societal standard for living. He did not have a disorder or condition that required their intervention. He was lacking pure nutrition and nature. He needed to reconnect with his ancestral heritage and acquire their wisdom. The public school system was not a place for him to find fulfillment. Rather than relocating to a natural environment, he was told he had a problem. Psychiatrists insisted this was inherited in his genetics. They informed us this was a wish from God for his cognitive functioning to decline in proportion with how many pills they instructed him to ingest.

Doctors and psychiatrists commonly blame depression on biology or genetics, and then prescribe medications to *boost* levels of dopamine, serotonin and norepinephrine. Often, the side effects from these drugs are creating more imbalances. Rarely do psychiatric doctors consider the role diet plays in the biology or make-up of the body. Most of these *experts* are unaware how important of a role maintaining a clean internal environment plays in overall mental well-being. They rarely mention a relationship with bacteria living in our gut.

An August 2011 study (64) published in *Gastroenterology* journal found that *gut bacteria and intestinal microbiota influences brain chemistry and behavior independently of the autonomic nervous system, gastrointestinal-specific neurotransmitters, or inflammation*. Researchers believe gut microbes communicate with the brain by modulating the immune system, or by producing their own versions of neurotransmitters. John Cryan, from *University College Cork* in Ireland, explains how the big nerve – known as the vagus nerve – which runs from the brain to the abdomen, acts as a *highway of communication between what is going on in the gut and what happens in the brain.* The health of our bowel, and the food and drinks that constitute our diet, have a significant impact on our attitude, behavior, feelings and mood. To assure we will not negatively alter our biological make-up, we want to be sure we keep our bowels clean and adapt a healthy, plant-based diet.

While mental health practitioners frequently blame genetics or neurological degeneration for dysfunctions associated with biological make-up, new studies provide evidence supporting diet, nutrition, and native plant medicines may play a more important role. Researchers have discovered compounds in raw fruits and vegetables can improve mood by altering biological make-up. A 2012 article from *Histories of the Neurosciences* journal *(65)* introduces the *monoamine theory of depression.* The article states, *"Billions of nerves in our brain communicate with one another through chemical signals called neurotransmitters. For the nerve cells to effectively communicate, they release chemicals known as monoamines."* Three of the most recognizable monoamines are dopamine, norepinephrine, and serotonin. Mental health practitioners prescribe medications to *boost* production of these neurotransmitters. The publication further explains, *as more monoamines are produced, an enzyme – known as monoamine oxidase – is produced to moderate and assure we maintain the right amount of these neurotransmitters.*

In a November 2006 study published in the *Archives of General Psychiatry (66),* researchers found that *people who are depressed appear to have elevated levels of monoamine oxidase in their brain.* This enzyme breaks down and balances neurotransmitters. When levels are elevated, numbers of neurotransmitters decrease. The study goes on to inform us there are phytonutrients found in spices and herbs such as cinnamon, cloves, nutmeg, and oregano, which inhibit production of this monoamine oxidase enzyme.

An additional study from the July 2011 *Journal of Neural Transmission* *(67)* explains how flavonoids, a group of phytonutrients found in apples, berries, grapes, kale, onions, green tea, and several other plant-based foods, may effect our brain biology enough to significantly improve our mood.

Along with fruits, herbs, spices and vegetables, there are plant medicines capable of reducing levels of monoamine oxidase enzyme. One particular plant grows abundantly in rainforests all over Central and South America, and is known as ayahuasca. This affluent vine is brewed into a ceremonial medicine that is a known monoamine oxidase enzyme inhibitor. Drinking this potent elixir breaks down the enzyme responsible for removing neurotransmitters. When people who are experiencing depression sit in ayahuasca ceremony circles, they are rewarded with instant relief of depressive symptoms. In these tribal communities, confrontation is resolved through prayer, music, nurturing, and by never placing blame on outcasts or scapegoats. Sometimes, all anyone needs is an opportunity for their voice to be heard.

In ceremony, all who join get a chance to speak. They open their hearts, release stagnant energy, and are empowered by a capacity to generate wisdom within. When we live in a community, we search for ways to integrate others into our way of life, welcoming diversity and offering opportunities for everyone to contribute and thrive. When someone is not well – whether they use drugs or proliferate violence – we teach them the power of tribe. By accepting them, feeding them nourishing foods, and allowing them the gift of speaking, we help them revert to their basic goodness. Today's limited system of support offers church, psychiatry, or rehabilitation for delinquency. These options provide no real solutions. The true healing remedy to depression is plant medicines, paired with a healthy lifestyle. Nature offers all of the abundance and cures we need. Coupling a pure lifestyle, void of poisons, with rich culture garners happiness. There is no sense of culture stronger than participating in plant medicine prayer circles. No lifestyle enriches health more than eating plant-based.

A March 2018 *Psychological Medicine* journal study *(68)* published the results of twenty-nine individuals who joined an ayahuasca ceremony. They were given a single dose, or similar-sized placebo dose. Each patient who received the ayahuasca reported rapid and significant antidepressant effects compared with those who were administered the placebo. In an August 2018 *Psychopharmacology* journal study *(69)*, fifty-seven attendants of ceremony were analyzed in Colombia and the Netherlands. They were interviewed before, the day after, and four weeks later. Ratings of depression and stress were both reduced significantly. This medicine is even being used to help rehabilitate prisoners in Brazil.

I wish my brother could have joined these prayer circles. I truly believe he would still be here with me today. I imagine him thriving while being immersed in this genuine culture. He needed community. He ached for his voice to be heard. His body was demanding nutrients that standard American foods do not provide. In a better paradigm he would have discovered plant-based nutrition, and plant medicines, and healed from his depression and pain.

In June 2012, the *Public Health Nutrition* journal published a study *(70)* in which researchers found eating vegetables three or more times a week can reduce depression by more than fifty percent. Imagine the benefits from eating vegetables three or more times *daily*. A May 2012 study in *Nutrition Journal (71)* suggests e*ating lots of fruits and vegetables may present a non-invasive, natural, and inexpensive therapeutic means to support a healthy brain.* There is concrete evidence showing the food we consume really does impact health, happiness, and intelligence.

A May 2012 review in *Nutritional Neuroscience (72)* suggests eating plenty of organic fruits and vegetables may *present a non-invasive, natural, and inexpensive therapeutic means to supporting a healthy brain.* Researchers found certain compounds known as polyphenols – which are found in abundance in plant-derived foods such as fruits and vegetables – provide a broad spectrum of molecular and cellular actions against neurological degeneration. Two specific polyphenols are EGCG – found in green tea and broccoli – and curcumin – extracted from turmeric. According to the review, *these two compounds are highly associated with higher cognitive function, better mood, and protective effects against various brain diseases.*

In addition, a 2008 study published in the *Neurochemical Research* journal *(73)* states, *"Dietary Factors have emerged as effectors of the brain by influencing cellular energy metabolism and modulating the signaling pathways of molecules involved with brain plasticity".* The study goes on to conclude, *"Food consumption and physical activity stimulate metabolic processes present in mitochondria – the main vessels of energy metabolism in the body that breakdown organic matter into usable energy".* Similar to the previous study, this research also highlights polyphenols, and encourages increased consumption of organic fruits and vegetables. Polyphenols were shown to have antioxidant and anti-inflammatory activity, and also to assist in reversal of neuronal atrophy and behavior deficits.

In a 2009 study published in *Oxidative Medicine & Cellular Longevity* journal *(74)*, researchers describe polyphenols as *natural organic compounds produced by plants as defense mechanisms against pathogen attacks, UV radiation, and physical damage. Over eight-thousand polyphenic compounds of plant origin have been identified – many of which are widely studied and recognized for their brain-protective properties.*

To enhance brain chemistry and regulate neurotransmitter activity, not only do we eat more fruits and vegetables, we may also need to avoid eating meat. Researchers are discovering chemical imbalances in the brain are associated with neuroinflammation caused by ingesting arachadonic acid. This acid is found primarily in chicken, eggs, beef, processed meats (hot dogs, sausages, bacon and ribs), fish, burgers, pork, and pizza. According to a cross-sectional study published in *Nutrition journal* in 2010 *(75)*, *arachadonic acid is a key substrate for the synthesis of proinflammatory eicosanoids and downstream cytokines. This can adversely impact mental health via a cascade of neuroinflammation.* In addition to arachadonic acid being present in animal-based foods, new studies are showing that meat and dairy-based diets cause intestinal microbiota changes that carry the potential for human enteric disease. *Harvard University* scientists report that *a diet high in meat and cheese – yet low in fruits and vegetables – alters the microbes living in the gut that influence weight, immunity, behavior, and mood.*

"Thoughts are an important part of your inner-wisdom, and they are very powerful. A thought held long enough and repeated often enough becomes a belief. A belief then becomes your biology." – Dr. Christiane Northrup

As Dr. Northrup exclaims, these thoughts do become powerful. As we cling to the belief that our depression is a genetic disorder and we have to live with unhappiness forever, this becomes our biology. This credence also enables us to develop dependencies on prescription drugs. We need to recognize we are not powerless over depression.

We have believed for too long that our biological make-up cannot be improved by any means other than chemical pills prescribed by psychiatrists or doctors. While conditioned to believe this, we rarely think to seek other expert opinions. We all want a quick-fix, so we rely on pills. Rather than get better, we let our health regress deeper.

We need to understand as a culture that chemicals in pills do not work synergistically with the human brain, and that ingesting these pills only worsens conditions. Our attention needs to shift toward what foods we are ingesting, how pure we are keeping our internal terrain, and what type of alternative therapies are available for people experiencing depressive symptoms. My program, *Soulspire*, offers cleansing, healing, and plant-based nourishment that can provide long-lasting relief from what causes sadness. There are numerous options available that can aid us in taking the steps needed to extend longevity and elude an early death.

Averting the Death Industry

There is a plot in this country to shorten the lifespan of every person collecting social security. This is accomplished through creation of disease using mechanisms such as adding chemicals to the food and water supply, promoting unhealthy foods as being nutritionally superior, and injecting viruses through various *immunization* shots. Once sickened to the point of helplessness, morphine is then gradually administered until the body withers and life force escapes. I witnessed this happen to three of my grandparents and my father. They each experienced symptoms of adapting poor lifestyle choices and dietary patterns. Their health problems could easily have been reversed if they had avoided medical intervention. They believed their conditions were hereditary, when in reality all sickness is either ingested or injected.

When farm animals die they are buried inside of the human gut to decompose, rot, and trigger formation of disease. When humans pass away they are injected with formaldehyde and other chemical preserving agents and then placed in wooden caskets where they will never decompose, nourish the soil, or be part of the circle of life. The *CDC* reported 2.8 million deaths in the United States in 2017. Nearly two million people are buried in caskets every year, and square footage of all cemeteries in the United States exceeds one million acres.

A 2012 *Berkeley Planning Journal* article (76) explains how the death industry butchers the environment. *The total amount of wood used for the caskets already buried in the United States requires trees from four million acres of forest – an area the size of the state of New Jersey. There are an estimated 115 million tons of casket steel buried in graves and 2.3 billion tons of concrete used for burial vaults. This is enough steel for two-thousand empire state buildings and concrete to pave a sidewalk to the moon twenty-eight times. Conventional burials in this country use thirty million board feet of hardwoods, twenty-seven hundred tons of bronze and copper, over one-hundred thousand tons of steel and 1.6 million tons of reinforced concrete annually.*

The egregious practice of preserving and sealing corpses into caskets and burying them is not environmentally friendly. Before bodies are locked in caskets, a chemical cocktail of formaldehyde, glycerin, methanol and phenol is injected through an artery to delay rate of decay. There are roughly eight-hundred thousand pounds of formaldehyde buried in caskets under the ground in the United States. Formaldehyde is a known carcinogen.

Of the million acres of land utilized for cemeteries in the United States, much of these sites maintain lawns with chemicals and fertilizers to keep the grass looking green and regulate growth of weeds. These chemicals seep into the soil and water below ground, harming insects and other species.

There are seventy-six million Americans expected to reach the age of the average lifespan in the next twenty-five years. If buried in standard plots, this would require one-hundred and thirty square miles of grave space. This is equivalent to an area the size of Las Vegas. To free up land we need to propose new ideas for honoring those who pass away.

Today there are pods we can opt to be buried in where we will breakdown into the soil and germinate the seed of a tree. As the tree grows, our remains blossom into this new life. There is also an option of buying biodegradable caskets. Indigenous rocks could be used as grave markers opposed to concrete vaults. A more appropriate selection is allowing your body to feed Earth, or the oceans, in a way that is sustainable for future generations. When my time comes on this Earth I wish to be buried beneath my favorite tree in Montgomery Woods in Mendocino County. I want my healthy body to provide nourishment for microorganisms, mycelium and soil to spring forth new life. Until that time I choose to prolong my life in the healthiest way possible.

To avert the death industry, the best strategies we can implement are abstaining from eating dead foods, befriending the sun, discontinuing the use of pills, eating vibrant organic foods, and refusing to use chemicals in our homes and gardens.

Restoring Ecological Balance

Similar to all other species, humans were once contenders on the same team with nature. We respected the land, collected and gathered food provided by Gaia, sheltered ourselves, planted seeds, and shared our music and love in tribes. Somewhere we were led astray, and as this idea of civilization was adapted and expanded into reality, we inherited disobedience, and became accustomed to abstracting energy away from nature for profitable agendas. By damning rivers, mining coal, drilling for petroleum and gas, installing wind turbines, and relying on nature for *power* we redirect energy and dismantle patterns aligned with nature. This leads to environmental collapse, extinction of ecosystems, loss of biodiversity, disharmony and civil unrest.

The magnetic North Pole is now moving from the Canadian Arctic toward Russia at thirty four miles per year (77). Smartphones use this magnetic power source for compass apps and GPS location. Air traffic control also depends on this magnetism. When the magnetic pole reverses this will upend communication and navigation systems.

In March 2018 SpaceX launched over four-thousand satellites into low orbit around Earth. As 5G technology expands, close to twenty-thousand more are expected to be sent up into orbit (78). This technology will use phased array antennas to emit powerful rays of radiation toward cell phones. New 5G phones will in exchange send radiation back. This atmospheric intrusion will collapse celestial bird tribes, sicken animals and humans, and inch us closer to the end game. All intrinsic patterns of living will be altered.

Migratory patterns of whales are ingrained naturally into their conscience. Birds are not errant in flight as they seek warmer climates, they are guided by a sense of direction inherent to their survival. All animals live in accordance with laws of instinct and they follow the power of nature manifesting through them. So long as their harmonious synchronization is not intentionally disrupted, they continue to play their role in contributing to the design of life here on Earth. Despite advancements in technology and biotech failures, man's pursuit to replicate the perfection of nature is not attainable. As we impede on every process we hinder the ebb of eternity and inch closer to complete devastation.

There are madmen who call themselves loggers and claim they *fall trees* for a living. Those same trees who stand tall for eternity, enriching us with life, are being decimated by confused people who never embraced the many facets of love. Their thousand year old roots are violently forced from the layers of dirt, clay, Earth, mycelium, life and organic matter that cling to them for existence. Hawks, owls and ravens are watching them destroy the only homes they have ever known. There is no balance remaining across the globe within the forest ecosystems.

On fishing vessels that litter nearly every body of water, men use nets, hooks and harpoons to terrorize marine life. They steal the food necessary for ocean ecosystems to survive, simply because they have grown estranged from their natural habitat on land. Men who have been stripped of their primitive awareness infest these boats and assault marine species. Captain Paul Watson warns, *Since 1950 there has been a forty percent diminishing of phytoplankton in the Ocean. Phytoplankton produces up to eighty percent of the oxygen needed to breathe. When Phytoplankton depletes, humanity will perish, and when phytoplankton disappears from oceanic ecosystems humanity ceases to exist.*

Oil and gas companies drill and frack offshore, leaving their waste to wash away into waves. There is no balance remaining in the ocean ecosystems. These black snake leaks pollute indigenous rivers. The shale rock is diminishing and Earth's core is beginning to experience fragility. A word to define this intrusion is idiocy.

Beached whales lay at rest on coastal shores. Their ear canals have been annihilated by sonar radars that send piercing vibrations across the seas in search for more oil we do not need. Harpoons burst through their flesh. Trawler nets scar their skin. They have few safe spaces left to swim.

The tallest mountain peaks are in jeopardy of being blown to smithereens by dynamite sticks that were planted to feed more of this disease that is greed. I watch calcium carbonate tears plaster the boulders that survive beneath, as birds mutter the saddest songs they will ever sing over coal mines that pollute the air and water we drink and breathe.

Farmers spray deadly chemicals all over the food they eat and sell as nourishment, on farms in every region of the world, believing this is somehow benefiting their operation. They have been tricked by lunatics who cannot ever appease their appetite for riches. The poison they are spreading seeps into water aquifers, saturates the supply of nourishment and inoculates every species with sickness and disease. There is little balance in our food system, and the collapse of bees, birds and insects is expunging a large percentage of what we can eat.

Rivers are enslaved by dams and stripped of their cleansing powers. Mother Earth can no longer cleanse herself because the power she diverts to her rivers has been stolen and claimed by man. The ebb and flow has nowhere else to go, and the contained tension is manifesting a change that could be a disguised blessing.

Earth's electric and magnetic frequencies have been intercepted by technology companies and the beautifully woven fabrics of life on this planet are tattered at the seams. Monarch butterflies are losing direction as they migrate. Soon we will experience the extinction of fresh air to breathe. A catastrophe with no solution is amassing. There is a disruption of ecological balance.

"The love of possessions is a disease they are sickened with. They take tithes from the poor and weak to support the rich who rule. They claim this mother of ours, Earth, as their own and fence their neighbors away. If America had been twice the size, there still would not have been enough." – Chief Sitting Bull

Gaia Frequency

She radiates a frequency that peace envies.

Her soul harmonizes with compassion only love knows.

This foundation constructing her being is substance the tallest trees breathe in.

Light is her heart beating.

Life persists as microorganisms, mycelium, smiles, soil, sunlight and water all united.

The pigments of a colorful planet vanish to a darkness that can be banished.

An army of unconscious allies competing to watch this world die is ingrained into a universal mind.

Wars dismantle every rising sun.

Washing up on the shores of every coast line are gravestones of slaughtered culture.

Guns turn strengths blind.

Bombs over Mosul.

Rivers running out of room to cry.
These dams are blocking freedoms.
Oil pipelines steal the tides.

Mindfulness matters in a world void of boundary lines.

Imprisoned Potential

Prison is the epicenter of torment and a foundational platform for negativity in this world to persist. The continuity of the prison industrial complex is synonymous with universal karma and the mistreatment of animals, oceans, plants, rivers and trees. For as long as living entities are locked in cages there will be disharmony on a planetary level. As forces of nature are misdirected to benefit human financial profits, there will be instability within societal organization.

America has the largest prison population of all countries in the world. Prison camps exist in this region and the people are poisoned daily with medicated water and genetically-engineered food laced with chemicals. America also has the highest rates of teen pregnancy, abortion, drug use, violence and release of toxic materials of any industrialized nation. For being declared as advanced, the statistics do not match the label. In Marianne Williamson's book, *Imagine (79)*, Stephen Lehman writes how judging, punishing and extending pain are each examples of counterfeit justice. *By dismissing inner experiences*, he suggests, *the external model of justice disconnects us from our soul's leadings and teaches us not to listen to the ways our soul speaks to us, or to honor the messages we get from living.*

Animals are imprisoned in factory farms, vivisection labs and zoos. They are abused, dismembered, mutilated, slaughtered and tortured. All over the world, humans experience similar suffering. People are removed from their homes daily and forced to live in cages inside of privately-owned prison systems. They are experimented on, fed poorly constructed substances formulated as food, and hydrated with water laced with prescription drugs, fluoride, rayon, chlorine and several other chemicals. To create a new paradigm free of this restraint, first we must abolish factory farms, end vivisection, and free animals from all zoos.

Oceans are castrated of marine life and held hostage by fishing vessels and trawler nets. Ocean currents are being extrapolated from their intended functioning to aid transportation of war weapons and machinery that is then used to efface more of the planet. Waterways have been imprisoned by corporations for resource distribution and financial gain. Crops are abused and misused for monocropping to fatten livestock and feed endless amounts of people who are undereducated on the real meaning of vitality. Current agricultural practices extract energy and land away from natural crop cycles and poison with pesticides. When fruits and vegetables are eaten without good intention and abused as stomach filler, the spirit force of these crops diminishes.

Nearly ever river in the world has been damned. The free flowing energy has been trapped, imprisoned and extracted for empowering technology. When rivers no longer flow free, innocence also derails and this confinement shells our potential to blossom and emerge as a species that does not contribute to the problems plaguing Earth.

Forests are clear-cut and trees are used for making furniture, paper and other products that can be manufactured using other material. After growing back the process is repeated. Trees can no longer grow freely without inevitably being cut down before the end of their life span. As a result we witness people dying before their natural life cycle expires.

The tension attached to surviving in the police state that has infiltrated global democracy is fierce. Every entity can now be labeled as a commodity and this strips the inherent freedom that was gifted with creation. A prison mentality is being artificially indoctrinated into select men and women to sustain the prison industry. This mental invasion also correlates with mental illness.

Jacque Fresco believed wholeheartedly that a transition to a global resource-based economy with free access to all necessities of life would reduce crime so effectively that we would not witness criminality. He urged us to return to a set of values that will enable us to survive. From his perspective, all of Earth's resources need to be declared as the common heritage for all Earth's people. This would avoid territorial disputes, liberate humanity from oppression, and free this planet from pollution and wars.

Power Struggle

Human nature is not congruent with conformity. The discontent, emptiness, and feelings of anxiety we experience are interrelated with domestication of the mind through inept education, corrupted culture, and incompetent values. As children are directed away from indigenous instincts, and institutionalized in public schools pushing agendas disguised as necessary knowledge, they acquire energy disorders and consciousness imbalances. Many adolescents and adults forge life paths through an acquisition of patterns woven from their upbringing and social environment, and from media, newspaper, radio, television and other means of technological intrusion. We map out our future from what we are told to see.

The shortage of leaders, mentors, and role models who are accustomed to living outside of the mainstream ideologies in which we are expected to integrate is problematic. Society is conditioned to idolize confused individuals who have gained notoriety through ennoble acts, but who are known and respected as possessing clarity. Those considered as leaders today are glorified with egoic entitlement to provide concierge services to corporations. They work with people who profit from the relentless pursuit to mine, log, poison and strip Earth of all resources and reserves of clean water. Sadism is culturally accepted and authorized by the people who truly should be responsible for eradicating this evil.

There is a global competition for energy escalating around humanity. Billions of people occupy this planet, utilizing energy from nature as they dance through life. Among the greatest sources for energy available to us are air, food, plants, soil, sunlight, trees, water and wind. Edible plant matter in fresh, raw form provides us with the richest nutrition. Eating raw fruits and vegetables elevates our radiant frequency. Pure water is a necessity. Sunlight promotes healthy skin and vision. Trees form canopies, protecting forest ecosystems that contain all elements needed for survival. When we vacate our desire for power and surrender to nature, we find companionship in the spiritual world. We discard struggle and inherit affluence.

Universal Karma

That anxiety you are being attacked by is the feeling factory-farmed animals are crippled with every moment of their existence. The claustrophobia equates to sea life being pulled from the water they depend on for survival. Sickness, and the diseases plaguing man, are symptoms of corroding dead animal parts that have been assaulting your esophagus and organs since the moment you were deceived into thinking eating meat is okay.

Bipolar disorder is Earth magnetism shifting through devices man-made. For every species that dies there is someone getting paid. Education robs indigenous knowledge from the human mind. Law enforcement raids the last of non-conformity, pushing this agenda to nullify our sense of individuality.

PTSD always results from something awful we see. These organized religions worship unjust deities to allow mankind to bomb for satiation of never-ending greed.

Earth feels the wrath of universal karma. There is a curse that has penetrated masses of humanity and is peeling away primitive virtues – stripping them of their dharma. The greed is insatiable. As beautiful nature is excavated and mined, the human mind develops holes, allowing microbes to takeover and implant thoughts of their own.

Millions of acres of land are burning. The smoke chokes up Earth's lungs and asphyxiates hopes of a better world. There are people who question the inherent right to life, yet they seem to be the ones in control. Every morsel of evil action carries a butterfly effect that diffuses more of the good that can be achieved. Being silent about atrocity is a guilty verdict, and you are the one who needs to stand up and speak out about what is happening to the planet we call home.

Billions of farm animals are abused, killed, raped and slaughtered to feed sick people. Their flesh becomes tainted with cancers and viruses. This death being consumed plagues all of mankind. Eating dead animal parts is not only wrong, but the opposite of ethereal. As man ends the lives of cows and pigs, more innocent people are bombed, shot and killed.

Amazonia is burning to meet the growing demands for beef, and to clear land for soy plantations to feed cattle. As this meat is ingested, humanity gets sicker. Chronic Obstructive Pulmonary Disorder (COPD) and cancer penetrates lung tissues of men and women. The lungs of Mother Earth are weakening similar to those of humans.

Close to seven-hundered thousand children die annually or are disabled from arms-related injuries that stem from wars. These wars are not always in poor countries where corporations are fighting to secure resources belonging to these regions. Much of the war ongoing today is within each individual human battling with their consciousness and desire for change. The darkness we acquire always faces resistance from the light we inherently shine as soldiers of the greater good. We are at war with ourselves, each other, corporate media, the medical association and oppressive institutions. We enlist ourselves to corruption and hatred as we buy in to a system devised to paralyze our sense of understanding life – as we do naturally when cleansed of all poison, pollution and propaganda.

As South Africa revolutionizes and fights to retain their culture, anger is also unleashed, and the dictatorial empire that stripped them of their native wisdom and peace collapses to the presence of justice. Many innocent people are dying in the process, some being burned alive, and in Malaysia and Indonesia orangutans and chimpanzees are also being charred to death as their homes burn to the ground for the extraction of palm oil.

Veganism will end this misery. Karma is not selective within a species. Animal agriculture is responsible for the worst genocide in history. Our mantra is a soliloquy. We speak for all beings. A plea for change, a demand for resistance and courage to speak even when no one else seems to be listening are our most effective tools for stabilizing peace and well-being.

"When one sits in the hoop of the people, one must be responsible because all of creation is related. The hurt of one is the hurt of all. The honor of one is the honor of all. Whatever we do affects everything in the Universe." – White Buffalo Calf Woman

Prayer For Awareness

Let us pray collectively.

We pray for not only the animal souls who are suffering from our careless acts, but also for what remains of the pristine rivers and land base being sucked dry of the plasma and blood – being petroleum.

Beneath every majestic and enchanted region is the blood – petroleum – and as we continue to drill for oil we lose more wonders of the world. We pray humanity will invest in alternative fuel sources so we can reduce our dependency on oil and to cease the fighting and end the violence attached to this resource.

The Arctic ice caps are melting at such a fast pace scientists predict they will be gone entirely within the next couple of decades. As they dissipate, we watch more beautiful species driven to extinction – being penguins and polar bears.

We pray to uncover ways to stop the ice from melting this year and to preserve this habitat forever. To protect the wholesome petroleum resting beneath the ice and to keep the carbon stored under from being released into the environment.

Rainforests all over Africa, Argentina, Bolivia, Brazil, Ecuador, Honduras, India, Indonesia, Malaysia and Peru are being decimated at a rate equivalent to multiple football stadiums every minute. We have lost eighteen percent of the Amazon region to illegal logging and eighty percent of this eighteen percent is for animal agriculture and palm oil manufacturing.

We watch as Sumatran tiger and orangutan numbers decline rapidly and both are on the brink of extinction. We can feel the souls of these animal brothers screaming into our bones, begging us to stop consuming palm oil and give up our addiction to flesh foods so we can eradicate factory farms and stop trading rainforests for cattle ranches and GMO soy, corn and wheat plantations that feed the livestock who never miss meals while children in Africa, Cambodia, India, the United States and regions all over the world continue to starve daily.

We pray for the sake of tigers, jaguars, gorillas, toucans and orangutans to stop treating trees as commodities and recognize each individual tree soul, honoring her trunk, chest and flesh by keeping the forests intact and thriving.

We pray for suffering chickens, pigs, cows, sheep, horses, buffalo, lambs, turkeys and other farm animals locked in dark crates for their entire existence in flesh all because we selfishly refuse to give up our addiction to eating flesh foods and think these sentient beings who bleed like us, cry like us, feel pain like us and love like us willingly give their lives for us to eat their tissues that construct the life force within them.

Truth is, we can all survive and thrive eating only plants. While plants are also living, the life force, minerals and phytonutrients within them continue to thrive once they pass into the human organism, while the soul of the animal escapes and life force is drained immediately after their life is taken.

Oil companies are responsible for leaking petroleum flowing into indigenous rivers in Central America. As these corporations carelessly poison rivers, cut down trees and force indigenous tribes to run away from the only homes they have ever known we are not only watching the animals go extinct in these regions, we are witnessing entire cultures being eradicated and murdered. Entire ways of life gone forever. Languages lost. Mothers, fathers, sons and daughters separated. Archaeologists predict fifty percent of the seven thousand languages spoken around the world today will disappear in our lifetime. May we pray for indigenous people to live in peace, for their cultures to be preserved forever and for the cleanliness of rivers and waterways.

In Africa, India, Thailand and other regions our beautiful elephant teachers are on the brink of extinction because poachers believe their tusks are worth more than their life, and of greater value than their right to have a face. The black rhino has become extinct for the same reason. We said goodbye forever to a beautiful species. We pray for these elephants, rhinos and poachers that coexistence and peace will be established.

We pray for Native American tribes who have been colonized and placed on reservations with no access to clean food and water that they will take their power back, start eating healthy, and stop feeding the same system that oppresses them.

We pray for what remains of North American rainforests. Each year the ancient redwood population reduces in size. These trees are being cut down to clear land for the expansion of the wine industry and for land to raise livestock so we can fuel the meat, dairy, and egg industries. We pray to understand globally why we do not need wine for good health, or meat, dairy and eggs for vitality. In truth that we recognize these compounds to be toxic and as contributors to poor health.

As trees in California continue to be devastated, and the drought gets worse, we are getting less rainfall since forests are responsible for generating rain. In addition, we are using over five trillion gallons of water annually – being pumped from underground aquifers – to sustain the dairy and meat industries in the region. We pray to universally switch to nut-based milks, cheeses and meat alternatives to shut down these industries and restore our aquifers.

Oceans are acidifying, starfish are disintegrating and the gray whale cannot breathe in her own home. Marine life is being over-fished, and we are sweeping with factory trawler nets areas the size of the Gulf of Mexico every year, a mile and a half deep. We pray for humanity to discontinue relying on fish and the ocean for food, and for us to start growing more organic fruits and vegetables to sustain life on land. We must protect our ocean brothers and sisters and the marine phytoplankton that provide up to ninety percent of the oxygen on land.

Finally, we pray to stop the biotech industry from distributing and growing genetically modified food and infecting every region with glyphosate. We pray to revert back to heirloom seeds from Gaia to restore balance in our ecosystem, eliminate pesticides and let bacteria, insects, mycelium and soil microorganisms live and practice their purpose – what they were created for.

We pray for all of life to find peace and resolution.

Give Africa Back To Her People

Corporate interests tell us we need to *help boost the economy* in Africa. To *provide democracy*, there is a widespread effort to install a Western education system on the continent teaching people how to live in a fantasy world based on the so-called *American Dream*. Indigenous people in Africa are disappearing fast. According to *Rights and Resources*, only *sixteen percent of total land in countries studied in Sub-Saharan Africa is owned or controlled by Indigenous Peoples and local communities (80)*. The other eighty-four percent is governed by multinational companies. Corporations are slowly taking over every region of this continent.

As each African country is robbed and stripped of their dignity, resources, and rights, the ethnosphere is damaged. Rather than preserving cultures that thrived independently for centuries before the corporate takeover, tribes are being forced to live in confined areas. Their water is sanctioned, and arable land is used to grow food for First World nations. Beautiful mountains and areas of land are mined relentlessly and stripped of metals and other resources to fuel growth of corporations in other nations. Children are forced into slave labor working in these mines. Farm land is used to raise cattle and other livestock to meet the demands of consumers in other countries. While over two-hundred million people are starving in Africa, billions of farm animals that never miss meals are raised in this region to feed people in other places. There is not enough food, land, or water to satiate the Hungry Ghost representing Western Culture. The result is poverty.

Poverty in Africa is not primitive to this land. I remember school textbooks teaching us that poverty is natural in Africa, and that this continent has always been infested with disease, sickness, and poor living conditions. Later in life, I learned that the reason why poverty exists in this nation is because Western interests are forcing an unsustainable lifestyle on the entire region that is illogical and irresponsible. African people are suffering, and through biological warfare, diseases are spread to depopulate regions of this continent.

According to Brookings, *the United States has invested fifty-four billion dollars in FDI stock and serves as the largest investor on the continent. There are an estimated six-hundred companies from the United States in South Africa alone. Between 2005 and 2017, Millennium Challenge Corporation (MCC) invested more than six billion dollars in fourteen sub-Saharan African countries through completed or ongoing compacts in infrastructure, health, education, and other sectors (81). China's role on the African continent has been defined by the financing of more than three-thousand largely critical infrastructure projects. China has extended more than eighty-six billion dollars in commercial loans to African governments and state-owned entities between 2000 and 2014.* These statistics help us understand why Africa went from being mostly indigenous and free of disease a century ago, to now being impoverished and stricken with illness. Corporations depend on their resources for business interests.

If we research causes of war over the last century in African regions, we notice a common theme. Each area where there has been civil unrest has been rich in a resource needed for financial gain. In Liberia we witnessed Civil war over tire rubber. South Africa was exploited for diamonds. In the Republic of Congo, Rwanda, and Uganda, wars revolved around coltan mining. The precious metal, tantalum, which is needed for all devices that connect to the internet, is extracted from coltan. Wars in Somalia escalated over oil. There has always been a pattern woven between war and abundance of resources in Africa.

Christian missionaries are utilized as instruments to downplay agendas, and children are intentionally injected with poisons and viruses in the form of vaccinations. Ebola and malaria are spread intentionally through vaccines to reduce population and easily gain control of these resource-rich nations. The best way to boost African livelihood, erase poverty, and assure good health is to remove corporations permanently from the continent, install clean water and effective plumbing systems, and give the food and land back to the people.

Nature's Law – Ecocide Is Illegal

Ecocide is any action committed by man that directly and intentionally harms the natural environment. The proposal of ecocide being categorized and enforced as an international crime was first introduced decades ago as a result of the exfoliation and damage caused by the chemical known as Agent Orange – which was used by United States soldiers in the Vietnam war. To be acknowledged as ecocide under this law, *the harmful effects on the environment would need to be long-lasting, severe, or widespread.* A 1996 article (82) submitted by Mark Allan Gray in the *California Western International Law* journal explains the parameters of this proposed law.

Every second, somewhere on this planet, ecocide is being committed. The burning of forests all over Indonesia and Malaysia for palm oil plantations is severe and long-lasting. The decimation of the rainforests for cattle ranches and GMO corn, soy and wheat operations is widespread. In Northern California the redwood forests are being plowed to the ground daily to open up land for grapevines as new wineries are constructed. Factory trawler nets are sweeping up miles of the ocean habitat routinely, obstructing everything in their path. Oil is spilling out of pipelines that were forced into sacred lands and polluting all water sources. Factory farms and feedlots are terrorizing our access to fresh air and clean water. There is no room to breathe for miles around the vicinity of areas contaminated with the feces and waste from this industry. Ecocide exists, affects all species, and needs to be stopped.

In 2013 the *European Citizen's Initiative to End Ecocide in Europe (83)* was launched by eleven citizens from nine European nations. The purpose of the initiative was to criminalize ecocide in order to abolish the extensive damage and destruction to ecosystems carried out by government-protected corporations.

In addition to the 2013 initiative, a proposal to amend the *Rome Statute* to include an international crime of Ecocide was submitted by Polly Higgins into the *International Law Commission (84)*. *Ecocide* was to be considered the *Fifth International Crime Against Peace*. If and when a person commits a *Crime Against Peace*, the *International Criminal Court* has powers to intervene in certain circumstances, even if the person or State involved is a non-signatory. If this amendment is to be passed in the *Rome Statute* all acts of ecocide in every nation could be enforced as crimes.

Today there are ten countries which have codified ecocide as a crime. In these countries ecocide is deemed illegal by law. The preservation of forests in these regions is placed first, before anything. In America the land we depend on for survival is treated as an enemy. We punish every source of nature impeccably.

To restore balance, America and all other nations must declare ecocide as illegal and abolish the practices of drilling, fracking, logging, mining and raising animals for food. All crops raised must be organic and free of chemical sprays. Production of plastic must be ended abruptly. Newspapers and other products derived of wasted paper from trees need to be placed out of print.

All impurities need freedom from existence. The idea of pills must be killed. Alcohol, coffee, cigarettes, fluoride and opiates are destructing our will to find purpose. Protecting the landbase we depend on for survival is among the most extravagant thrills.

As we learn to respect all of nature in correlation with how we praise our higher power, or creator, we begin to counter-program mentally and destabilize from the stronghold grip that has been suffocating our brains from adequate cognitive functioning. When we disrespect nature we abuse the God we worship.

"Regard Heaven as your father, Earth as your mother, and all things as your brothers and sisters." – Native wisdom

Great Spirit Is In All Life

Lakota Natives perceive our creator as a Great Mystery who loves all unconditionally. They call this spirit Wakan Tanka. Throughout history, tribes all over the world have carried unique perspectives of how life on Earth formed. In Western Society, the belief is that one man embodied God, and compiled a book of teachings through his Prophets that would stand as a basis for how we live. If we disobey this word, we are castigated to a place known as Hell. This precept that the creator of all life only lived as a human, through Jesus, exemplifies the myth of human supremacy. Mankind is not the only creature protected by God. Jesus has resurrected trillions of times in animal, bacterial, fungal, insect and plant species. God has lived as a cow, horse, jaguar, gorilla and pig. This Great Spirit rides on hawk wings through the vast sky and dangles on yellow Aspen leaves that dance in Autumn sun. This energy has taught other animals the way of God, just as Jesus is believed to have done with humans. This entity instructs seeds to germinate, sprout and blossom into fruits, plants and trees. Every step on unscathed forest soil massages the soul of God resting in each atom of nature.

These politicians who are self-proclaimed *Christians* and claim to love Jesus would have condemned this man during his reign. If he crossed the border today, the current presidential administration would have him arrested and deported. He would likely be stripped of his rights, imprisoned, and persecuted for teaching his ways. What if Jesus again resurrected as man and nobody knew because the President had him arrested and imprisoned in a *tent city* to await his deportation back to a place where he is not rooted? There is neither race nor class differentiation of humans. He who feeds the contradiction of this scripture is sinning at a level that is unforgiving.

God's vitality depletes to sounds of chainsaws. Sadness is echoing in the consciousness of the working man – he who earns a living by destroying what is truly alive. Cultural conditioning teaches those who are unaligned to neglect what is right and embrace all that is wrong. Man commits crimes against humanity then expects forgiveness from sins in cities void of bird songs.

There is a hole in God's heart the size of Earth Mama's scars. The pain emulates from white owl's eyes, watching the trees she calls home as they crash into soil, paralyzing mycelium from running. Microorganisms die on impact. Thousands of years of magic are smashed. The hurt will always last.

There is a hole in God's soul the size of a broken family. As big as my daughter's smile. Larger than unjust marijuana laws and the oppression of a prison cell. The shovel takes another dig. Oil rigs drill deeper into the surface of our existence and livelihood and Great Spirit still believes in our good.

There is little truth in ministry. Pastors and priests preach sermons of nonsense, influencing armies of wasted potential to contribute to the death of each part of God destroyed for their diet and material belongings. Churches are places of worship just as forests never logged by man. To attract a spirit of the most high, inner purity must be acquired. No angelic beings desire attachment to those who ingest evil. Some priests and preachers are praising a Holy Spirit that is a mask on a demon. They hide behind the ugliness they store within and use their prestige to prey on kids. They are no servants of Jah's kingdom. Time will always expose them.

Those who have integrated scientific pantheism as a core belief know that nature is a source of peace and beauty, as well as the focus of our care and vigilance.

Our intent with spirituality can progress toward attracting energies that cling to goodness rather than acquiring demonic forces that drive us to kill, poison, pollute and be sickened. The presence of your higher power in your life broadens and is enriched when you provide a healthy terrain, infected only with purity, for this entity to reside within. As we continue to ingest impurities we are driven further from reaching our pure potentiality as sovereign beings. This is a path to extinction.

"Great Spirit is the flash of a firefly in the night. The breath of a buffalo in Wintertime. The little shadow which runs across the grass and is lost in the sunset." – Cherokee Wisdom

Sixth Mass Extinction

The spirit of the grape crop, along with corn, soy, wheat and several others is being depleted of vitality as a result of mass production from humans. Even watermelons are losing taste. Globalization thieves the energy from our food. Forest spirits suffer in anguish as trees are bulldozed to the ground to pave way for more soy, corn, wheat, wine and livestock. River spirits are weeping as flowing water carries poisons from animal agriculture, chemical manufacturers, and wineries. Animal spirits have been tortured far too long and are suffering. Perhaps though, the most damaged of all is the spirit of humanity – those responsible for planetary degradation. Mankind is gravely ill. Parasitic leaders govern laws and mindless lunatics dictate education.

Trees, rivers and indigenous cultures are endangered species. As we hug the last black rhino, we tell him we are sorry that this species of man takes pride in vandalizing all other forms of life. There is a permanence attached to saying final goodbyes. Elephants, orangutans, polar bears and tigers wait closely in line. Their only hope is gaining their habitat back from this alien species known as man.

We are losing cultures to corporate land grabs, deforestation and diets that are not sustainable. Mothers, fathers, sons and daughters are being wiped from existence. Tribal legacies stripped from Akashic records. Whoever passed the staff to the angry, confused man and blessed him with power has let him speak for far too long.

A June 2018 study published in PNAS Journal (85) reveals that eighty-six percent of all land mammals are now livestock or humans. This analysis found that only thirty percent of the birds in the world are wild, while the other seventy percent are farm-raised chickens and poultry. Researchers also reported that eighty-three percent of wild mammals and eighty percent of marine mammals have declined, along with fifty percent of all plant species. The cause of these drastic rates of decline are human activity. Mass deforestation, mining, commercial fishing, and drilling for oil and gas is depleting this planet of everything needed to maintain a healthy balance.

In May 2019, the *Intergovernmental Science-Policy Platform on Biodiversity and Ecosystem Services (IPEBS)* held a week-long meeting to discuss the role humans play in the decline of biodiversity and diminishing planetary health. This group of over four-hundred scientists met in Paris, France and compiled a fifteen-hundred page report *(86)* for the UN as a result of their three year investigation. The findings include information from over fifteen-hundred scientific references. In their assessment they note one-million of the eight-million species on this planet are nearing extinction due to animal agriculture, deforestation, illegal hunting, pesticide use, and shrinking habitat.

The report indicates that humans are ravaging the planet by displacing forests, grasslands and other nature reserves with farms, cities and other developments. This results in a shrinking habitat insufficient for sustaining animal and plant life. In addition we are overfishing the world's oceans, with one-third of the world's fish stocks already collapsed. Humans are also permitting climate change from the burning of fossil fuels and greenhouse gas emissions from feedlots and factory farms. This climatic change makes weather conditions too hot, wet or dry for some species to survive. The pollution of the land and water from erroneous agricultural methods, drilling, fracking, logging, mining and pesticide use is depleting fresh water reserves. Finally, the report lists another threat being the allowance from humans of invasive species to crowd out native plants and animals. These species are mainly cows, pigs, and other farm animals, along with deer that are overpopulated as a result of humans hunting the big cats and wolves.

The chair of the IPBES, Robert Watson, summarized by saying, *The health of ecosystems on which we, and all other species depend, is deteriorating more rapidly than ever. We are eroding the very foundations of our economies, livelihoods, food security, health and quality of life worldwide.* Humans may be the most invasive species of all.

In response to this report (87) a senior attorney with the *Natural Resources Defense Council*, Zak Smith, said, *This report should help us understand that the signals of natural ecosystem* collapse are symptoms of our collective human patterns, including consumption, resource exploitation, and inequalities in economic and political power. The only way we are going to save our planet and ourselves is if we firmly break with the failed systems of the past and embark on a new human journey.

In August 2019, the *Intergovernmental Panel on Climate Change* released a report compiled by over one-hundred experts to address the worsening global climate crisis (88). Researchers addressed the devastating impact of accelerating rates of deforestation in tropical rainforest regions, and insist that *efforts to curb greenhouse gas-emissions and the impacts of global warming will fall significantly short without drastic changes in global land use, agriculture and human diets.* The special report *describes plant-based diets as a major opportunity for mitigating and adapting to climate change, and includes a policy recommendation to reduce meat consumption.*

We are facing the sixth mass extinction, witnessing armies of new-growth souls scavenging the ethnosphere. They are drinking, smoking and drilling holes in the ground deep enough to bury their formaldehyde-ridden corpses inside of caskets that were once cores of beautiful redwood trees being cut down to facilitate greed. We live among unaware platoons of cowards who have been sedated by these manipulated visions of going to war to gain power. The most important war that never took place was the one to gain back all that has ever truly mattered – being our landbase.

This is the time to disfigure gas-fueled vehicles. There is no space left for hatred and the evil committed to secure crude oil is cruel. Rhinos and elephants are not going extinct solely because of poachers. Some of the richest resources rest beneath their turf. Humans could save them but are too sedated to let corporations be defeated so instead wander lost into the last of the beautiful animals extinction.

"Treat Earth well. This land was not given to us by our parents. The air, resources, soil, and water are loaned to us from our children. We do not inherit Earth from our ancestors. We borrow this land from our children." – Native Proverb

Old Growth Forest of Your Soul

I am desolate in a crowd of beautiful people looking for familiar eyes.

I feel isolated in cities of misunderstanding.

Emptiness fills me on this planet full of conflicting perspectives of how life should be.

I scavenge the damaged ethnosphere, searching for the old-growth forests of your soul.

Pieces of enchanting memories of the serenade of your laughter fill my void.

I still hold you in fairy tales of undying love while my passion is inflamed with happy vibrations that are reflections of your heart as she beats for me, inhaling your butterflies, and exhaling forever under meteor showers of never-ending affection.

I am watching an abundant night sky full of luminescence.

Constellations are strumming broken guitar strings trying to mend the hollow sounds of life without you.

A galaxy of stars that still do not shine like the aura that surrounds your muse.

With every flowers new bloom, I see your smile.

Your pheromones are nature's perfume.

In the distance I feel closer.

Separation molds us into abundance.

On this remote island with only darkness I am finding hope in the light that our memories hold.

I am sailing off into the perfect storm, knowing when the confusion ends you will teleport back into my arms.

We will evolve into organic farms.

Our immortal sorrows will feed happiness to the children of tomorrow.

The bond we share will last forever and nourish the soils.

Peace will grow from the roots of our unity.

In another universe Gaia tells love stories of you and me.

Resource Redistribution – Circulating What Remains

Our demands for a surplus of material attachments not relevant to our survival hinder our chances of surviving for many more generations. We are disconnecting from the harmonious flow of life, allowing distractions to set us back from proceeding on the course of our evolution. Eating manufactured food saturated with chemical additives, flavoring agents and preservatives that dim our shine further and cultivate a lack of introspection leads to our intellect growing estranged from human nature. How can we collectively shift our consciousness and phase out the mistakes we have engraved into the foundation for this poorly constructed civilization?

Profit, coupled with greed, is enemy number two – in regard to poor distribution of resources – behind overpopulated cities. To satiate the demands of a single large city how many resources are required from areas all over the world each day? What definitive plans of action can we strategize to reduce the demands and create sustainability in cities? The dualutions are found in eliminating dependency on animals for food; growing food within cities using rooftops and abandoned lots; denying availability of non-renewable resources to encourage production using recycled materials already in distribution; banning newspapers and plastic; and converting to solar energy.

How do we ethically and morally control the surging population without using covert methods of population control? The current paradigm of introducing alcohol, cigarettes, drugs, meat, dairy, eggs, processed foods, psychotropic drugs, cancers and viruses, cell phones and 5G technology, food chemicals, genetically modified foods, and prisons – then watching everyone get sick, suffer and die – has been successful to an extent, but they are not sustainable solutions and only lead to further planetary degradation. The mass-mindedness generated by mainstream media mastery has society revolving around a lifeless cycle of misery that leads to premature death and costs our planet too many resources. The population control specialists need to devise better strategies.

To effectively combat the rapidly growing population we need to consider which species' growth we want to curb. Are the approximate seven billion humans inhabiting the Earth leaving a global footprint larger than the trillions of farm animals being raised for food all over the world to satisfy the erroneous eating habits man has adapted? Two acres of land are required to raise one grass-fed cow for slaughter. After two years this animal is manufactured into a few hundred pounds of beef – a food known to increase risk of developing heart disease, cancer, Alzheimer's, arthritis, diabetes and nearly every disease afflicting man. A well designed permaculture farm could produce 140,000 pounds of food on the same two acres in just one year. 280,000 pounds of food could be produced in the same span of two years using the same area of land needed for three-hundred pounds of *grass-fed* beef. Why is over half of the land on the forty-eight lower states of the United States being used to raise animals for food when we could use a fraction of that to grow nutrient dense plants, feed everyone on the planet easily and drastically reduce pollution from animal agriculture? Which is more sustainable, tens of thousands of pounds of fruits and vegetables or a few hundred pounds of beef?

If we divert the energy and resources we use to raise livestock and produce dairy toward growing organic fruits and vegetables for satiating hunger we can figure out a new paradigm that will save this planet and free up more land for myco-reforestation. Rather than focusing on how we can wipe out populations of people by poisoning them with alcohol, cigarettes, drugs, GMOs, pills, cancers, diseases, viruses and other means of killing without violent force, we can instead expend this energy and time educating people on how to eat plant-based, stop contributing to pollution, grow their own food and say no to evil.

The heart-breaking percentages of land being used for animal agriculture points to our greatest threat and number one contributor to resource scarcity. There is no possible way to meet hunger demands in cities with animal protein. The supply of dairy, eggs and meat products in cities can no longer be provided if we wish to establish resolution. Animal-based foods must be banned from cities without any hesitation or leniency. Milk from cows must also be phased out. With advances in technology and our capacity to transport goods, the availability and diversity of nut and seed milks and meat alternatives discards the dairy and meat industries as obsolete. The World Bank and Government systems can bail out the farmers in this industry and write checks to cattle ranchers and dairy farmers for ten years of salary to relieve them of hardships attached to the abolishment. These farms can then be used for growing food in a prosperous way.

The introduction of laws enforcing gardens on rooftops are also needed for each family to find the means to feed themselves without depending on corporations for nourishment. By educating people with the wisdom of permaculture no being will ever go hungry again. Permaculture is a permanent culture designed to last forever which crafts ecologically sustainable living systems that provide food, nourishment, pure water and shelter for communities. These systems are capable of providing ten-thousand times more food from plants on small fractions of the land being used for animal agriculture. By utilizing arable land using this sustainable approach, not only do we free up land for communities and families, but we also drastically reduce pollution and protect forests and wildlife.

"Trees are sanctuaries. Whoever knows how to listen and speak to them can learn the truth. They do not preach learning and precepts. They preach, undeterred by particulars, the ancient laws of life." – Herman Hesse

Knowing over five-hundred thousand trees are cut down simply for each Sunday's newspaper to be printed reveals we can no longer afford to continue this ecocidal process. In total, newsprint consumption in the U.S. in 2009 accounted for nearly ninety-five million trees, around 126 billion gallons of waste water and emissions in the range of seventy-three billion pounds of greenhouse gases (89). Nearly four billion trees are cut down around the world each year for paper. If we simply refrain from buying newspapers we could save a lot of trees. If we were to recycle all newspapers this would save millions of trees each year. Simple choices such as these help to elevate our consciousness. If we want paper the material used for production must be recycled. If not then we cannot have paper. All packaging for products must be derived from compostable material – preferably bamboo or hemp. Plastic, Styrofoam and cardboard (unless recycled) is no longer an option.

In February 2019, the *Natural Resources Defense Council (NRDC)* released a report, T*he Issue With Tissue: How Americans Are Flushing Forests Down The Toilet (90)*. The information provided explains how toilet paper has an irreversible impact on Canadian Boreal Forest. This publication describes how each time we flush conventional toilet paper down the toilet we are essentially disposing of parts of majestic, old-growth trees that have been violently ripped from the ground. These forests being decimated are home to over six-hundred indigenous communities, billions of songbirds and several species of endangered animals. These celestial tree beings also store carbon in the soil they rest above. In fact, for hundreds of millions of years forests have been regulating greenhouse gases and converting carbon dioxide to oxygen for the sustainment of life on land.

We learn from this report that more than twenty-eight million acres of boreal forest – the size of the state of Ohio – were logged between 1996-2015 for tissue pulp to manufacture paper and tissue paper. The tissue market generates thirty-one billion dollars in revenue annually and they accumulate these profits from virgin wood pulp – opposed to using recycled pulp or sourcing from bamboo or hemp. The boreal region in Canada stores more carbon than all currently accessible coal, gas and oil reserves combined. According to the NRDC report, this forest intact removes the amount of carbon dioxide equivalent to the annual emissions of twenty-four million passenger vehicles yearly. Detrimental and irresponsible logging of boreal forest emits hundreds of millions of tons of carbon into the atmosphere each year – all for us to flush down the toilet.

In addition to boreal forests, the region of forests extending from Appalachia to the Florida panhandle have also been decimated for tissue and paper. These trees are used for the production of twenty-seven percent of the world's paper products. More than half of the remaining trees in this area are less than forty years old. The United States alone uses over nine billion pounds of toilet paper annually. This high demand not only paves the way for mass deforestation, but is also responsible for the release of chlorine and dioxins into the environment that are used in the bleaching process. To effectively support an impactful alternative, buy bamboo products, or choose recycled and chlorine-free paper. Bamboo grows back twenty times faster than trees and releases thirty percent fewer greenhouse gases.

"We need acts of restoration, not only for polluted waters and degraded lands, but also for our relationship to the world. We need to restore honor to the way we live, so that when we walk through the world we do not have to avert our eyes with shame, so that we can hold our heads up high and receive the respectful acknowledgment of the rest of Earth's beings." – Robin Wall Kimmerer, *Braiding Sweetgrass*

For an entity to qualify as an endangered species and be included on the *Endangered Species List* the following questions are asked: Has a large percentage of the species vital habitat been degraded or destroyed? Has the species been over-consumed by commercial, recreational, scientific or educational uses? Is the species threatened by disease or predation? Do current regulations or legislation inadequately protect the species? Are there other manmade factors that threaten the long-term survival of the species?

Never has there been a more qualified candidate to make the list than trees. Only a small percentage of native forests still stand today. A large percentage of this species vital habitat has been degraded and destroyed. Yes, trees have been over-consumed by commercial uses. Yes, trees are threatened by predation. The predator is greed-driven humans who think decimating the most beautiful forests is okay. There are no current regulations or legislation adequately protecting trees from endangerment. The manmade factors threatening the long-term survival of this species are logging trucks, chainsaws and other devices used to clear-cut forests – to go along with desensitized brains. Each tree in every remaining forest qualifies as an endangered species. Every flowing river can be listed as endangered. Shale rock which stores natural gases is also being driven to the point of endangerment.

Forests are not the only victims of human confusion and corporate intrusion. Mountaintops are also being blown apart for coal mining to provide electricity in an unsustainable way and rivers are being imprisoned by dams for hydroelectric power. To divert away from these egregious practices, solar panels must be installed for every building and housing structure. Government grants should be provided for solar companies to implement these panels. New jobs will emerge as the demand for workers grows in careers related to regenerating land, cleaning up areas contaminated by coal mines, remediating forests and dismantling preexisting dam structures.

Perhaps more so than greed and profit denial may be our most threatening enemy. We can no longer neglect the dire need to restructure the livelihood of civilization to coexist in peace with the soul of nature. By permanently eradicating the process of raising animals for food; banning commercial fishing, whaling, and dolphin slaughter; prohibiting the distribution and manufacturing of dairy, eggs and meat; and criminalizing hunting we take the first steps toward establishing hope for sustaining future generations.

There are astounding masses of junk congesting civilization that needs to be put through recycling. When items are simply taking up space in homes and there is an overload of stuff in one room then there needs to be some sort of dictatorial voice determining what gets put back into the mix. We are overproducing too many things. This clutter fuels sickness.

Our initiative now is to teach about growing our own food; the link between our lifestyle choices and betterment of the planet; alternative fuels; solar energy; and how to live peacefully without causing harm to any species anywhere in the world. We need to divert away from this path we have been directed toward which leads to doom and slowly shift to aligning with the harmonious flow of nature that will help us bloom.

Timber Falls – The End of Logging

Mother tree opens her womb and gives birth to love for all species. She blesses us up with oxygen and caters us with compassion. She is resiliency standing strong.

White owl's iris pierces man's sleeping eyelids. He awakens in an enchanted forest. He sees bobcats struggling to survive and mountain lions nearing extinction. A raven caws at him a message too deep for his shallow understanding, letting him know his job falling trees is devastating her family's home and those crashing trees paralyze our soil.

Mankind is on a conquest, occupying every forested region on Earth with heavy machinery, logging trucks and men who have lost their righteousness. Logging corporations have an appetite for destruction that can never be appeased. They use dishonesty, genocide, manipulation and violence to clear-cut beautiful ancient forests wherever trees reside.

These heavy machines condense and compress forest soil, which omits air space for the oxygen roots need to grow and spread. This increases the susceptibility of roots to pathogenic invasion. Compaction of soil leaves scars on forest ecosystems that last for decades. Soils that have for centuries and millennia been held safely beneath forest compost become exposed to rain and sun as a result of scarification (91).

After the complete ravaging of forest ecosystems, the left over remains of trees and brush not used is burned in piles. This process exposes and sterilizes soil, removes protective soil cover from the underlying roots, seeds, and spores, and volatilizes soil nutrients such as nitrogen and sulfur. Bulldozing the burned piles deprives much of the area of nutrients remaining in ash. These charred soils are even less permeable to water (92).

My Native American ancestors built their homes from scraps of fallen trees. Cutting down forests was never an option in their culture. The Sacred Tree was always revered as a gift of life. Our ways teach that the health of each forest is a reflection of the health of those living in or near the forest. Today over ninety percent of all old-growth forests are gone, and comparably, close to ninety percent of the population is sick.

Jacoby

In *Strangely Like War (93)*, Derrick Jensen writes of how *the United States has close to five-hundred thousand miles of logging roads running through the national forests alone. This is enough road to drive back and forth from Washington DC to San Francisco one-hundred and fifty times. Over two-hundred thousand acres of forest are cut daily around the world. This is an area larger than New York City. Seventy-eight million acres are deforested every year. This is bigger than the country of Poland.*

Jensen further explains that *these logging roads are the primary source of soil erosion and landslides in disturbed forests. Sediment discharge results in flooding, erosion, landslides, lowered water quality in streams, scoured and destabilized stream beds, and property damage. Studies show that logging roads trigger debris avalanches that accelerate erosion twenty-five to three-hundred forty times beyond that in intact forests.*

The majority of cleared forest land is used for animal agriculture, palm plantations and wineries. We do not need to eat animals, cook with palm oil or drink wine to sustain life. In fact, all three of these options are contributors to poor health.

Forest and management are two words to never be in the same sentence, let alone merged together as a declaration of human authorization and responsibility. Trees are an endangered species. Their livelihood is not to be dictated by man.

The organizational principles guiding Indian civilization are rooted in the biodiversity, harmonies and nature of the forest. They worship Aranyani – the Goddess of the forests and primary source of life and fertility. They see the forest as a community, and this is the premise of their primitive model of social evolution. The culture of their forest is known as the Aranya Samskriti. The forest is recognized as the highest expression of Earth's fertility and productivity. She is symbolized as Vana Durga – Tree Goddess (94). All over the world there must be a shift to this type of forest dedication.

Mankind is gasping for a taste of purity and liberation.

Gasping For Freedom

I have lung cancer – a terminal illness.

The only way to cure my malady is if my Dad quits smoking. Each drag he takes robs my lungs of oxygen.

I have a collective disorder that stems from the self-inflicted abuse and careless choices I made during adolescence.

No matter how healthy I am, a team is needed to heal this demon.

I hear my remedy is pure oxygen pumped deep into my core, but greenhouse gas emissions from animal agriculture are too heavily saturating our air.

I have a breathing epidemic destined to end me, and I have been informed I can recover only if the powers that be first agree to stop forcing vaccines on innocent Africans and Indians.

I have a lung disease that will not release me until I can hold my beautiful daughter in my arms again and show her the love she will never receive from any other man.

Cancer is mutilating my beautiful flesh as I write this and I am suffering like the great ape, orangutans, chimpanzees, gorillas, koalas, pandas, macaws, wild parrots, hawks, vultures and eagles watching their homes being destroyed to logging.

Deforestation is robbing my oxygen so immensely I can barely breathe.

Indigenous cultures are disappearing like my lung tissues are decaying and languages are vanishing.

Humans are going extinct because greed keeps taking over in a land where man leads with his head instead of his heart.

Jaguars, tigers, wolverines, and bobcats are so endangered if we applied any more pressure the world might burst at its seams.

I am gasping for air, trying my hardest to breathe, and all of these fools keep buying cigarettes begging to fall victim like me.
My grandmother lost her life to meat, cigarettes, dairy, processed foods and pharmaceutical poisoning.

Her body was begging for oxygen and the pulmonologists kept supplying her with synthetic air laced with carcinogens.

My brother took his own life because he was poisoned for far too long in the form of psychotropic pills and psychiatrists prescribing him evil.

Something keeps telling me my capacity to breathe will not be revitalized until humanity finally accepts the only real combatant to sickness is optimal nutrition from plant-based purity.

I will suffocate until all of society quits smoking.
My lungs are crippled.
My soul is shaking.
My spirit is a flame that cannot burn its brightest until I feed this essence with food for fire, being O2.

Redwood forests are going extinct, and mountain lions and ravens are battling the same disease.

Gray whales cannot breathe in their own home.

The acidifying oceans are real, not make believe.
Starfish are literally disintegrating.

We need to stop factory trawler nets, harpoons and dolphin slaughter just as badly as we need to give up our addiction to meat, dairy and eggs and let the animals and marine life roam and swim free.

I have a lung situation that refuses to leave.

She will only part ways if humanity awakens, turns off the TV, and starts to see the genocide taking place behind the corporate medias flashy big screen.

My breathing will not get better unless the Amazonian rivers can flow free and pure.

I will continue choking until the white buffalo and wild horses can live on their land for free, not being submitted to execution or slavery, or having to battle with cattle herds being mass bred in factory farms for their chance at survival.

I am crying the black rhinos last tears.

I am weeping like the salmon flapping in shallow rivers damned for energy sources the sun provides to us for free.

I am sulking with the Eastern cougar spirit.

I am feeling the white owls pain.
My lungs are collapsing like albatross packs and the penguins and polar bears homes, as the Arctic ice continues to vanish.

This cancer is spreading into my bones.
I am cracking apart like the Earth's core from fracking wells and oil drills.

My diagnosis tells me the culprit has metastasized to my brain and is spreading like forest fires intentionally ignited for palm oil manufacturing.

My lungs have holes that will not close until the savages who call themselves hunters stop killing the wolves and leave the bears, deer and wild boars alone.

These deep trenches will not be filled until all poaching ends, we save the elephants and rhinos from extinction, and we stop terrorizing the antelope, gazelles, leopards, lions and zebras and simply let them be.

This deadly condition is stinging me, and Great Spirit tells me the pain will not subside unless we stop wiping out the bees and insects with neonicotinoids, glyphosate and pesticides, and learn how to plant heirloom seeds and grow organic fruits and veggies.

My chances of surviving look grim, and unless we stop waging wars over religions, using missionaries to cover up the syringes, and placing innocent men, women and children in prisons over a facade called the war on drugs, I am afraid there are a limited amount of days left I will be living.

This cancer is my stress eating at me. I am dying and the only way to keep me alive is for all of humanity to detach from evil and find peace and freedom.

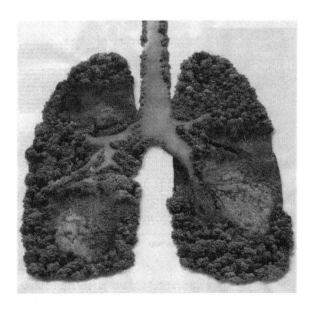

Let Me Cleanse – Global Dam Removal

The pigmentation of money. Shades of skin. A rainbow's beautiful spectrum. The iridescence of sunlight. These all mean nothing when the color of water is not pure. Rivers are endangered species. There are millions of dams in the United States alone. Nearly one-hundred thousand of these dams are at least thirteen feet tall. A combination of the re-routing of streams, occupation of river water for agriculture and fracking, hydroelectric dams, and pollution from mining and oil operations is depleting the free flow of Earth. Dairy, meat and wine production suck aquifers dry. Lakota natives use the phrase Mni wichoni, meaning water is life. They recognize rivers having the duties, liabilities, powers and rights of a legal person.

Similar to how humans are dependent on the health of their lymphatic system for cells to regenerate efficiently, Earth needs her rivers to flow free for cleansing from the chemicals being dispersed everywhere by unconscientious consumers and profiteers. Today only one-third of Earth's largest rivers are free-flowing. When rivers are damned the planet cannot heal or regenerate. When humans stagnate their lymphatic system with alcohol, animal-based foods, dairy, pills, processed foods, shots and tobacco products they also are incapable of healing. The damage is reciprocal. We learned from Chief Seattle's words that we only damage ourselves when we destruct the web of life.

Damn removal projects are to multiply rapidly and mankind must work together to replace energy sources that were once dependent on hydro-electric with solar power. Gradually the rivers will be restored without human dominion over them. Animals and plant life who depend on free-flowing rivers for survival will replenish and thrive in abundance.

Sunlight provides enough nourishment and resourcefulness for the planet to operate in prosperity. Each morning and every evening we are to worship this beautiful star, pledge our allegiance, and give thanks. Now is the time to transition away from energy sources that deplete Earth.

Jacoby

Frack Off – Keeping Gas Underground

The process of *fracking*, or *hydraulic fracturing*, involves the fracturing of rock by pressurized liquid to release gas. A fracking fluid is used that consists of an undisclosed combination of close to a thousand toxic chemicals and thickening agents, sand and water. This cocktail mix is injected with high pressure into a well-bore to create cracks in deep shale rock for natural gas to be released. Trillions of gallons of water are used annually by this industry. When injected deep into the ground this fracking cocktail mix contaminates underground water aquifers and permanently damages the water supply. Residents who live near fracking operations often experience brown water coming from their faucets and in some instances have demonstrated how they can ignite this water with open flame from the flammability. In areas where offshore fracking operations are taking place thousands of dolphins, fish, whales and other aquatic mammals wash up to shore no longer alive. Starfish even disintegrate from the acidity and toxicity.

While propane has been used for decades as an efficient fuel to heat homes there are much cleaner, safer and more ecologically-friendly sources for heat. Consumers too often disregard, or are unaware of the environmental and health implications attached to this business. What many people do not understand is the process of fracking requires large amounts of water to be orchestrated. This water is contaminated with a mixture of undisclosed chemicals known to be hazardous and which have even been linked to respiratory diseases.

Western States Petroleum Association, accounting for eighty percent of the oil and natural gas drilled in California, announced their companies fracked 628 oil wells in 2011 – about a quarter of all oil and gas wells drilled across the state that year. A 2009 report by the *Groundwater Protection Council (95)* states that *the amount of water needed to drill and fracture a horizontal shale gas well generally ranges from about two million to four million gallons, depending on the basin and formation characteristics.* With roughly twenty-five hundred wells being fracked annually in the state, and each well requiring up to four million gallons of water, total water usage for fracking in California alone is close to ten billion gallons. Imagine how much water this equates to all around the world. California is only a fragment of the land being exploited for natural gas globally.

What may potentially be worse than fracking itself is the fact that one-third of the *natural gas* retrieved from this industry is being wasted because they do not possess the necessary storage equipment to collect all they are releasing. This is known as gas *flaring*. Additionally, the majority of gas which multinational corporations are extracting from the ground in particular regions is being shipped off overseas to other areas of the world. Gas companies poison the landbase in one region, exposing them to massive amounts of carcinogenic chemicals, then export what they loot to other nations. These people occupying the land where fracking happens do not receive any of the profits accumulated. Their only acquisitions are the harmful consequences.

If we can find alternative energy sources to replace propane we will help provide a surplus of water to every region. We will also save thousands of plant and animal species from exposure to the chemicals from fracking. Phasing out hydraulic fracturing will benefit all life on Earth simply at the expense of corporations who are generating trillions of dollars in profits from drilling. To compensate companies who have invested in destruction equipment, financial and governmental institutions can bail them out and reimburse them with guarantees they will relinquish the practice and discontinue the ecocidal activity.

"Change happens by listening and then starting a dialogue with the people who are doing something you do not believe is right. Lasting change is a series of compromises, and these compromises are alright as long as your values do not change." – Jane Goodall

Preserve My Blood – No More Drilling

In April 2019, the indigenous Waorani community in Ecuador won a court case ruling that the land they occupy for their livelihood cannot be auctioned off for sale to oil companies. These beautiful men and women live in the upper headwaters of the Amazon River region, which is deemed as one of the most biodiverse rainforests on Earth. Their territory expands over two million acres and is home to over two-hundred species of mammals, six-hundred bird species, nearly three-hundred fish species and thousands of insect species. These lands constitute one of the Upper Amazon's last intact wildlife sanctuaries. Sadly, the petroleum industry has recently opened roads for oil platforms and pipelines into the heart of their sacred land. This corporate pursuit is a commonality in sacred spaces around the world.

In 2012 the *Ecuador Ministry of Energy and Non-Renewable Natural Resources, Secretary of Hydrocarbons*, and *Ministry of Environment* decided to sell indigenous land to oil companies without consulting tribes prior to the transaction *(96)*. As a result Amazon rainforest was divided into sixteen different oil blocks and put up for sale in an international oil auction. After years of court battles justice was finally served. Nemonte Nenquimo, a plaintiff and representative of the *Coordinating Council of the Waorani Nationality Ecuador Pastaza*, announced: *Today, the courts recognize that the Waorani people, and all indigenous peoples, have rights over our territories that must be respected. The government's interests in oil is not more valuable than our rights, our forests, our lives.*

The fight is still ongoing however, as oil companies are still attempting to gain access to nearly half of a million acres of their land. The time is now for all citizens of this planet to work in synergy to protect sacred lands and preserve what is left of the most beautiful places on Earth.

A January 2015 Nature journal article (97) details the work of researchers from *University College London*. They used detailed data and highly proficient economic models to demonstrate how change is needed to prevent global temperatures from rising two degrees. Scientists concluded that *vast amounts of oil in the Middle East, coal in the US, Australia and China, and many other fossil fuel reserves will have to be left in the ground to prevent dangerous climate change.*

To prevent this climatic change we learn that eighty-two percent of the remaining coal reserves must be left alone and untouched. In addition, we must not consume forty-nine percent of the gas underground or thirty-three percent of the oil. The present economic model in place ignores this imminent information and defies all life on this planet.

A lawsuit was filed in 2015 on behalf of a group of brave and courageous children, *Juliana vs. United States*, to block the United States government from continuing the use of fossil fuels (98). The case consists of twenty-one plaintiffs from ten different states. The non-profit legal organization behind this action is *Our Children's Trust* – directed by Julia Olson. The discovery includes over thirty-six thousand pages of evidence and argues that the government has proven incapable of dealing with climatic change and has failed to protect the nation's air, coastlines, forests and water. The plaintiffs present valid evidence proving the government has known for over fifty years that burning fossil fuels would cause climate change – dating back to a report from former president Lyndon B. Johnson in 1965 which declared climate change as a catastrophic threat.

In the book, *Intelligence For Earth (99)*, Robert David Steele defines catastrophe as *what happens when humans do not plan for or respond to, and then either over-react or under-react to the long-term implications of what would ordinarily be nothing more than an isolated disaster*. For over fifty years now, under the least effective leadership, the human clan has not adequately planned for or responded to the crisis attached to oil exploitation.

Our Children's Trust is demanding that we all are afforded our right to a climate system capable of sustaining human life that is fundamental for a free and ordered society. For decades we have been poisoned and stripped of our inherent rights to clean air, land and water by corporations profiting from the extraction of oil. Today the blueprints exist for a new paradigm which could easily phase out oil-dependent vehicles and modes of transportation using other sources of energy.

In addition to *Our Children's Trust, Earth Guardians* is a youth-organized group of activists who are actively working to combat the use of fossil fuels. They use *art, music, storytelling, on-the-ground projects, civic engagement, and legal action to propel change within global communities*. This organization has thousands of engaged leaders across six continents devoted to finding alternatives to dirty energy, and creating solutions to the many problems plaguing the environment (*earthguardians.org*).

One liter of spilled oil can contaminate one-million liters of water. When leaked from pipelines oil spreads over the ground surface in a thin layer that denies oxygen to animals and plants. This process disrupts the food chain and cycle of life in ecosystems, harms animals, insects, microorganisms and soil, and prevents photosynthesis in plants. Leaking petroleum not only poisons drinking water, but also degrades water necessary for irrigation to sustain crops needed for our food supply.

Today is a potent day to make a difference by helping to raise awareness. We can all work together to demand clean-fueled vehicles, and abruptly end the exploitation of Earth for a resource that should never leave the ground.

"We can all experience a feeling of deep admiration and love when we see the great harmony, elegance and beauty of Earth. A simple branch of cherry blossom, shell of a snail or wing of a bat – all bear witness to Earth's masterful creativity. Every advance in science deepens our admiration and love for this wondrous planet. When we can truly see and understand Earth, love is born in our hearts. We feel connected. That is the meaning of love: to be at one." – Thich Nhat Hanh

A Soulful Plea

I wish I could wake up in a world where cigarettes do not exist. I would pump fresh oxygen, straight from the nucleus of ancient redwood giants, into the cracked and decayed cancerous lung tissues of smokers to let them feel what fresh air tastes like.

I wish they knew their condition was not only a result of smoking, but also from their organs being discombobulated by the infusion of toxic debris lying dormant in processed foods and animal protein.

I want to live knowing the blue whale is no longer suffocating in her own home because we poison her habitat with plastic, petroleum products, animal excrement saturated with methane, and oil driven wars – to benefit shallow egos of those who never found love.

Let me reside in a world where my only fear comes from how my daughter will react to me sneaking up behind her and chewing on her little baby feet – while she breastfeeds and fuels with her beautiful mama's sweet pure nourishment.

I want to feel safe knowing I can send her away to a public school system that will not infiltrate her brain with mistruths and nonsense, or serve her genetically modified remnants of really bad ideas that never should have developed to the sapling stage – all while confined in prison-like buildings that represent the police state we are subjected to.

I seek to exist in a world where fresh wild blueberries free from genetically-engineered greed and pesticide contaminants can be my cup of coffee.

I want to live in a land where people actually drink water, not the bottled up residues of fracking chemical waste pumped from sewage pits, then micro-filtered and ozonated to be served to billions of gullible people who gave up their right to having access to clean water to an industry collapsing from being built on deceit.

I want America to take back her throne, eliminate logging, and let hemp again grow – the way nature intends. We can let disabilities be recognized as strengths and use them to defeat all weakness.

I desire a society where television lies are still elements and resources untapped in mines. I envision solar powered roads, hemp homes and petroleum-free transportation. I propose free education for all without corporate agendas and a structure where prisons actually help reform people – by this I mean teach them how to live outside of a world of slavery and feed themselves from nature, not from packaged, processed ready-made items.

Healthcare can start on our plates, and in plant-based organic school cafeterias where we teach kids the truth – not that meat is protein, but that animals are life and factory farming is cruel and must be abolished.

I live in a world where animals are my friends. They have families too. They each possess a heart and soul. They breathe through cleaner lungs than we have. They know their roles. They do not destroy, they only love.

This is the planet I want to encompass and navigate on my life's journey. I no longer want prescription drugs, cigarette smoke and alcohol to murder any more families. I want true health and prosperity for all. I do not seek a piece of the fortune. I only want to know I changed lives with my purpose.

I refuse to see the sixth mass extinction, or be a part of the problem, so I strive to unite a real union that will clean up this evil polluted mess that wars, drugs, money, power, and bombs have distorted and let the pristine roots shine crystal clean.

I want to save the planet from Satan's misunderstanding problem and his deranged thought process that somehow makes him think treating souls as objects or products is okay.

Mountains Are Not To Be Mined

In addition to oil reserves, rivers, shale rock and trees, mountaintops are disappearing fast enough to coal mining that they could also be classified as endangered. There are over fourteen-hundred pits of coal ash in the United States alone. In addition to coal, bauxite is a mineral-rich rock that is the primary ore for aluminum. Phosphate is also mined for pesticides. Mining devastates the land, water and health of people in surrounding areas. Researchers have determined that ninety-six percent of groundwater near these mines is contaminated with toxic poisons. In nearly every state close to one-hundred percent of the coal mine operations tested are leaking toxic waste into nearby streams and sources of water.

The ideology that humans have a responsibility to manage resources and dictate nature is more accurately correlated with idiocy. Forest *management*, *sustainable* oil production, and *natural* mining are all oxymorons. Man has no intrinsic governance over petroleum, rocks, water or trees. All resource management is fictitious.

Humans who believe they are aiding nature with destruction need to be immersed in a hyperbaric chamber filled with a type of celestial awareness that could awaken them to perceive the destruction they are responsible for as is – not as some pretty title they paint in place. Their awakening requires several ayahuasca sessions and a transition to a plant-based lifestyle. They need a series of colon hydrotherapy sessions to flush the plaque coating their intestinal walls. This would be of great benefit to them and could help them awaken to the severity of how detrimental their actions are to Earth.

While there are claims that mining somehow *strengthens economies*, this is far from the truth. When we poison people, destroy land, annihilate ecosystems, and permanently denature water sources this does not strengthen anything other than the profits of affluent corporations.

Ocean Clean-Up

According to the *Center for Biological Diversity*, *studies estimate there are now up to fifty trillion pieces of plastic in the world's oceans — from the equator to the poles, from Arctic ice sheets to the sea floor (100). Not one square mile of surface ocean anywhere on earth is free of plastic pollution.* With the dire need for plastic production to cease, the petroleum industry is pushing to continue the mass manufacturing of this waste product. The *Center for Biological Diversity* reveals that *the fossil fuel industry plans to increase plastic production by forty percent over the next decade. These oil giants are rapidly building petrochemical plants across the United States to turn fracked gas into plastic. This means more toxic air pollution and plastic in our oceans.*

Halfway between Hawaii and California lies the *Pacific Garbage Patch.* This is a vortex of trash that is visible from satellites up in space and is believed to cover an area up to 1.6 million square kilometers. There are an estimated 1.8 trillion pieces of plastic debris in the pile (101). Fish in this ocean ecosystem are estimated to consume up to twenty-four thousand tons of plastic each year. The plastic causes severe intestinal injuries that are often fatal.

Irresponsible humans endlessly consuming products derived from plastic contributes to this mess daily. The collection of plastic in the oceans is overwhelming marine life and drastically depleting ocean ecosystems. Some areas of the Pacific Ocean have a seventy-to-one plastic-to-phytoplankton ratio. Most of the oxygen we depend on for survival on land is generated from the plankton in the oceans, so as more plastic piles up we inch closer to asphyxiating ourselves.

Ocean dead zones are expanding and marine species are going extinct at a faster pace than ever before. The pH levels of the world's oceans are becoming more acidic each year. This results in the disintegration of starfish. Sea birds are declining because their food is being over-fished and when they ingest plastic waste that is mistaken as food this minimizes the storage volume of their stomach – causing malnutrition and starvation.

Some dead whales that wash to shore are found to have over eighty pounds of plastic waste in their stomach. Ninety-eight percent of albatross studied were found to have consumed some type of plastic debris. The plastic waste is driving dolphins, fish, sea birds, sea lions, sea turtles, seals and whales to the point of severe endangerment.

A comprehensive review from the *Marine Pollution Bulletin* journal (102) portrays how plastic pollution in the oceans affects at least seven-hundred marine species and kills around one-hundred million marine mammals annually. Plastic in the oceans is expected to outweigh all fish by the year 2050. To save marine life, and essentially all life on Earth, more energy must be diverted toward cleaning up these large bodies of water.

In 2019 a device invented by a young man named Boyan Slat and carried out by a non-profit called *Ocean Clean-Up* will begin cleaning the plastic from the oceans. In the first five years the project is expected to clean up half of the garbage patch in the Pacific Ocean, with a capacity to remove 150,000 pounds of plastic per year. Once the plastic is removed the duty will be ours to discontinue the manufacturing and production of more plastic. The boldest and most effective way we can demand the end of plastic is to abstain from using all plastic products.

"Remember, always, that the nature of a warrior is to act. Do not be daunted by the formidable strength of the opposition. Do not be depressed by gloom and doom predictions. A true warrior must welcome challenge and transform the impossible into possible. While living in these trying times, your task is to confront situations created by human apathy and ignorance, and focus your actions through love for the future and all of the children of all of the children of all species." – Captain Paul Watson, *Sea Shepherd*

A Spectator

The people are corrupted with drugs.
A counterfeit culture forces them to hide as they make love.

Too much of mankind seems to be sleeping through life.
With a frequency this low, how could anyone claim to be high?

We are in need of a universal awakening.

I am a scavenger picking at warped minds.

A passenger, observing these action-less actors as they play the roles of successful people.

They are nature-deprived and nutrient-deficient, with bellies full of pig meat, living in an illusion.

Their egos leak toxic waste, aiming to dictate, hollow-out, and suffocate the landbase.

I am trapped here, navigating these broken images that represent people.
I watch as they climb higher into the hierarchy's social Army.
Their arrogance pads their comfort.

They loathe in fortunes they have accumulated from raping the less fortunate of their water, land, metals and food.

They have committed genocide and wiped out entire cultures from their so-called 'living' rooms, where they pollute their brains with television lies, eating processed foods, and breathing artificial air into their heart-diseased instruments that conceal darkened souls.

These are the folks who live on the hill.
Those John Lennon warned have learned to smile while they kill.

I make myself invisible.
I do not want to be seen.
Embarrassed by what 'my people' have managed to be.
Now I see we are far more dangerous behind the scenes.

They do not show you what ecocide really means on mainstream.
The oceans are acidifying.
Forests are disappearing.
All water sources are drying.
The wild animals are dying.
People do not perceive Main Street from an honest lens.

Families are suffering, and children are enslaved in other nations for stock numbers to increase.

All so a select few can get a 'piece' of life 'above' poverty.

You do not know terrorism until you understand truly their agenda overseas.
They seized Libya's oil.
They stole Iraq from her own people.
All under the guise of freedom.
In a democracy you should not have to be reminded you are free.
You will know when the chains are loose, violence only tightens the noose.

I am a bystander, looking through a foreign lens.

Fighting for peace is like playing the lottery to eat.
A war against terrorism is like giving methadone to heroin addicts.
War is terror.
Hurting others is a shallow man's creed.

So why are they bombing Afghanistan for their gold, and for opium we think the economy needs?

To supply the pharmaceuticals for those who are GMO-diseased?

This is only feeding the "War on Drugs."

The reason why one in twenty-eight children only see Mommy or Daddy through glass once a week.

They do not get a chance to touch, or feel their love, and grow up empty.

Ten percent of people over eighteen are locked in institutions with no fresh air to breathe.

They are now products of the prison industry.
I call this cruelty.
The time has come to change the way they are doing things.

Marijuana is arguably the most powerful medicine on the planet.

Yet, the law still demonizes this beautiful plant, and destroys the lives of those in possession.

Meanwhile, the gas companies are blasting chemical cocktails deep down into our water supply.

They are rewarded with cash prizes.

As an eyewitness, I observe, and have seen.

Executives collect the profits and buy prostitutes to sniff lines of coke with.

Their children and wives wait in their giant homeless houses, another night without Daddy, the usual.

Mommy numbs the sadness with another glass of wine.

The young ones feel emptiness inside.
"He'll take us shopping the next day, and that will make things all okay."

More stuff they do not need at a cost they will never truly see. When there is not a line of gullible people waiting to 'buy' they call this a housing crisis.

The real crisis is millions of families are living on the streets while banks own enough empty houses, abandoned buildings and structures to shelter everyone in need.

I am a spectator watching others walk around in thick layers of ignorance.

They keep them plastered on by covering themselves with lotion, perfume and make-up.

By eating food responsible for planet degradation.

Smoking cigarettes, drinking alcohol and relying on medical doctors to 'treat' them to heal their pain.

This only takes them further into sedation.

Botox does not only take away your beautiful smile, this procedure destroys your true nature.
This perfection you are seeking is conditioning you for failure.

Animal agriculture poisons every compound on the planet.
I watch as each day new species vanish and rainforests disappear.

More cattle, more chickens, more pigs, less water, less land, less trees.

All so the rich can get their fix while their lifestyle nurtures disease.

As an onlooker I am saddened by what I see.

As animals die their natural defense mechanisms wait dormant in their flesh.
With each mouthful you swallow they wake up inside you and release the suffering you inflicted on them.

This is real vengeance.
This is cancer.

These folks pray to be saved as they ail.

Pay all of the money they stole along the way right back into the system they were feeding with no shame.

Monetary wealth cannot rescue them now, karma always gets them back one day.

I see them pointing fingers but they are the only ones to blame.

Vanishing of Icebergs

When *Glacier National Park* was established in 1910 there were one-hundred fifty glaciers within the park. Today there are fewer than thirty remaining and these glaciers that remain are a fraction of the mass they once were (103). At the current pace of liquefaction these remaining glaciers will be gone within thirty years. For ten-thousand years nothing happened to the ice in Western Antarctica. Now, after only one century of mankind's notorious mistakes, the ice is disappearing. Most Central and Eastern Himalayan glaciers in India are expected to melt within ten years. Rising temperatures from excess carbon released into the atmosphere as a result of animal agriculture, deforestation, drilling, fracking and mining are responsible for these vanishing glaciers. The melting of ice is associated with eroding coasts, rising sea levels, sinking land and temperamental storms.

In 1995 the *Intergovernmental Panel on Climate Change* issued a report projecting the sea level to rise up to thirty-seven inches by the year 2100 from thermal expansion of oceans coupled with the melting of glaciers and ice sheets (104). Today, over twenty years later, the EPA reports that sea levels have risen up to eight inches in the last century. We are losing thirty-five gigatons of ice each year and the outpouring of water flowing out has nearly doubled in the last thirty years.

Antarctica is the main ice-covered landmass in the world, containing around ninety percent of the world's ice. If all of Antarctica's ice melts, sea levels will rise nearly two-hundred feet. According to the *Sustainability Ninja* and *NASA (105)*, up to two-trillion tons of ice in Alaska, Antarctica and Greenland melted between 2003 and 2008. This equates to four-hundred billion tons of water each year, or over twelve-thousand tons of water running into the oceans every second – enough to fill five Olympic swimming pools. In place of the beautiful glaciers that once mesmerized all who witnessed these spectacles are sand, silt and emaciated penguins and polar bears. Even if you do not believe this will have an impact on you please think of future generations and be mindful of your footprint.

Saving Orangutans – Ceasing Global Palm Oil Production

Oil palm plantations cover more than twenty-seven million hectares of Earth's surface. Land cleared for palm oil plantations annually is equivalent to three-hundred soccer fields. These green deserts containing zero biodiversity now cover an area of land the size of New Zealand. Rainforests all over Africa, Latin America and Southeast Asia are bulldozed daily for new plantations. Close to sixty-six million tons of palm oil is produced annually for animal feed, biofuel, chemical products and processed foods. Not only is this product endangering the planet and imperiling several species, palm oil also contains fatty acid esters that are known to damage human DNA and trigger cancer formation.

A 2016 *Duke University* study published in *PLOS One* journal *(106)* found that palm oil is extracted in forty-three countries with eighty percent derived from Indonesia and Malaysia. Existing plantations were discovered to have been the driving force behind forty-five percent of deforestation in Southeast Asia and over thirty percent of decimation of forestland in South America. Of all regions impacted, those of gravest concern are in Ecuador, Indonesia and Peru.

While armed militias of programmed men in police uniforms protect oil palm corporations over indigenous people who live in forests, the Shipibo people are forced from their homes in the Peruvian Amazon. Over five-thousand hectares of their ancestral land has been destroyed. Sarawak's forests in Malaysia are being slashed and burned in the Mulu region. The Borneo region is suffering a similar fate as Hiroshima – only without nuclear warfare. Borneo elephants, orangutans and Sumatran tigers are being driven to extinction. If you listen you hear piercing cries of howler monkeys and macaws. Tree frogs are falling silent. Palm oil production is an international crisis and this product is not necessary for our survival.

Make the choice today to abstain forever from purchasing products that contain palm oil.

Enlightened By Gaia

Pachamama, climb deep into my soul.

Bring your plant medicines and let them serenade through my veins.

Attack the uncertainties.
Cripple the doubts.
Shatter the stress that eats away my well-being.

Penetrate me with vengeance and force me to awaken my spirit that is life force.
Breathe into my lungs air from your inner core.

Oxygenate me with your purity.
Detoxify my blood.
Caress my lymphatic vessels.

Bless me with your angelic melodies and embed your lessons deep into my foundation so I will never again question my connection to your roots.

Let me speak my truth and equip me with values that cannot be denied.

Drown me in your rivers of knowledge.

Give me strength in my voice so I can utilize my vocals to teach this society that is sleeping through extinctions and dumbed down by fluoridated lies and pharmaceuticals there is more to life than the American Dream.

Help me enlighten us all to put the dollar aside, awaken our conscience, and better understand our purpose.

Empower us to drop the bottle and catch some truth.

Lead us to the fountains of Peruvian power so we can drink awareness and escape the corporate media's noose.

Unite me with the black jaguar spirit and tell him to look into my soul and prepare me for all I ever need to know.

Let me bleed world peace.
Use the tears that fall free from my soul to nourish your cells.
Permit the mycelium to drink from my being.
Urge the microorganisms to feast on my footprints.

Fill your needs from my undying disease I know as love, love, love.

Teach me how to love without conditions.
Embrace me with your wizardly wisdom.
Captivate me with all of the things money cannot buy.
Saturate me with honesty.

Do not ever let me forget the many facets of your beauty that go beyond your stunning face and striking features.

Awaken me with love.

Love me so deep I find ways to alkalize the acidifying oceans.

Suffuse us all with the solutions we need to repopulate the canopy of the Amazon region.

Nurture me with your warmth that emanates from purity.

Bless me with your elixirs that fix me as I feed from your never-ending passions.

Bulletproof my temple so this energy will always last.

Love me in ways that stimulate my imagination.

Open me up to your forests so I will never be lost again.

Glypho's Hate

"From the cradle to the grave glyphosate is deeply problematic. The environmental costs begin with mines that destroy thousands of acres of habitat critical to the survival of imperiled species, and end with a pesticide that harms all life." – Hannah Connor, *Center for Biological Diversity*

A *glyph* can be defined as *an alphabetic font or other symbol that pictures an encoded character;* or as *a graphic symbol that provides the appearance or form for a character.* A graphic symbol that can be painted out as a result of the application of glyphosate around the world is *the hate for all life.* A *glyph of hate,* or *glypho's hate* – is representative of the death of all life in and emerging from the soil. The chemical glyphosate embodies this hate for all life as the substance is used to gradually poison all life on the planet.

A 2015 geological survey (107) conducted by the United States *Food and Agricultural Organization* determined that 2.6 billion pounds of glyphosate herbicide was sprayed on agricultural land in the country between 1992 through 2012. Additionally, a February 2016 *Environmental Sciences Europe* study (108) revealed that Americans applied 1.8 million tons of glyphosate since the introduction in 1974, and 9.4 million tons have been sprayed worldwide onto fields. This equates to more than two-thousand Olympic-size pools in water weight, or enough to douse nearly half of a pound on every cultivated acre of land in the world.

In February 2019, *Science Direct* published the results of a study (109) showing positive correlation between exposure to glyphosate and Hodgkin's lymphoma cancer. The research was conducted by five scientists at *University of Washington.* Their results show glyphosate exposure increases risk of developing cancer by up to forty-one percent. Several lawsuits are now being filed and plaintiffs are being awarded billions of dollars for the damages they incurred from this chemical.

The prevalence of childhood diseases, debilitating conditions, life-threatening illnesses and neurodevelopmental disorders has surged since the mid-1990's. In proportion to the rise in degeneration is the application of glyphosate. In 1987 approximately eleven million pounds of this chemical were sprayed. This number gradually increased over the last three decades to three-hundred million pounds being applied annually. The only other explanation for the upsurge in ailing people is the introduction of the reckless new vaccine schedule for children – with kids now being inoculated with forty-six shots through childhood compared to only six shots when the nation had healthy children.

Glyphosate is the main ingredient used in the most popular herbicide on the market. This poison is derived from a mine. After phosphate ore is extracted the substance is manufactured into elemental phosphorus. This constitutes the base for most fertilizers and pesticides. The extraction process removes soil from mountaintops, destroys vegetation, contaminates water and causes extreme air pollution. Much of the glyphosate used is mined from a remote corner of the southeast region of the state of Idaho in the United States. This area is referred to as the *Phosphate Patch*. Over seventeen thousand acres have been exploited to this date for the manufacturing of this savage chemical. The *Greater Yellowstone Ecosystem* and *Yellowstone-To-Uintas Corridor* are affected by the mining of these phosphates. This wildlife corridor is three-hundred fifty miles long and connects the *Greater Yellowstone Ecosystem* with Utah's *Uinta mountains*.

Dr. Zach Bush explains in a Podcast with Rich Roll how glyphosate is a water-based chemical that seeps into the water supply and does not go away. He suggests if we were to stop spraying glyphosate today all over the world, fifty years would be needed for Earth to cleanse from this onslaught of poisoning. Today is the day for us all to gather collectively and stop using this chemical.

Silencing Crickets – Global Insect Decline

Many South American tribes believed the chirping of crickets brought good luck. In Native American culture, butterflies were thought to be messengers from spirits of ancestors and loved ones. Some tribes even associated colors of butterflies with different meanings. White butterflies visited to bring good fortune, light, and purity to the tribe, while blue butterflies carried wisdom and intuition. Insects were always revered as important until the introduction of intensive agriculture. An April 2019 publication in *Biological Conservation* journal *(110)* found that over forty percent of insect species are endangered to the point of extinction from habitat loss due to the diversion away from wild food toward intensive agriculture, and the use of agro-chemical pollutants. This comprehensive review of seventy-three historical reports on insect decline around the globe released statistics on insect biodiversity loss that are astounding.

Half of the world's moth and butterfly species were found to be in decline. In the Netherlands eleven of the twenty most common butterflies declined from 1992 through 2007 and the range of over seven hundred day-flying moths declined in eighty-five percent of species between 1980 to the year 2000. Half of the bumblebees analyzed across three-hundred and eighty-two locations in the United States declined by up to ninety-six percent in the last thirty years. The United States recorded six million honeybee colonies in 1947 and over the last seven decades that number has reduced by sixty percent to just over two million. The decline in honeybees began immediately after the government approved the organochloride chemical DDT for agricultural and medical uses.

There has been a recorded seventy-six percent decline in the flying insect biomass in Germany. The Puerto Rican rainforests experienced a ninety-eight percent loss of biomass. These numbers are startling. Insects comprise roughly two-thirds of all terrestrial species on Earth. Earth depends on these creatures for pollination and they even naturally maintain balance among pests. Banana slugs, beetles and earthworms recycle nutrients and process animal waste. Everything in the forest and soil ecosystems work synergistically to balance life and assure continuity.

Spraying for mosquitoes wipes out large percentages of insect populations in areas where the poison is spread. These chemical cocktails are not designed to solely kill mosquitoes, they wipe out everything in their path. When municipalities spray to control pests they are demolishing ecosystems. This is referred to as *Integrated Pest Management (IPM)*. Microbial larvicides such as bacillus thuringiensis and bacillus sphaericus are used to bind to receptor cells and degrade the gut microbiome of flying insects. These toxins can also alter the bacteria in human and animal species. Adulticides such as methoprene are used to mimic growth-regulating hormones in insects and prevent maturation of insect larvae. When municipalities spray these compounds to control mosquito populations, they degrade the quality of life for birds, fish, humans and several other species of insects as well. These IPM programs also drain marsh water levels to stop breeding of mosquitoes.

The draining of wetlands and swamps for animal agriculture, fracking, insect control and wineries is a huge threat to the survival of insect populations. Without bugs there can be no food, and without food all life perishes. To combat this issue the published review authors suggest we must change our current methods of producing food. If we refuse, insects as a whole will go extinct. Habitat restoration and a drastic reduction in agro-chemical inputs are effective ways for stopping further decline. In addition, rehabilitation of marshlands and improved water quality are needed. Implementation of effective remediation technologies and for reducing runoff contamination are required.

A single dragonfly is capable of eating over one-hundred mosquitoes in a day. They also eat large numbers of mosquito larvae in larval form. Bats can ingest up to eight-thousand mosquitoes in a night. By planting a variety of plants which dragonflies are attracted to and keeping forests intact for bats to thrive we can effectively control mosquitoes.

Rates of Soil Erosion

"The foundation of chemical agriculture and chemical fertilizers rest on the assumption that what a plant removes from the soil can be analyzed and replaced in chemical form, but fails to take into account the complex biological processes and mechanisms through which the chemical transactions are performed, and aided by finely tuned and highly specialized living organisms whose operations cannot be duplicated or even completely understood". – Deborah L. Martin, *The Rodale Book of Composting*

Topsoil is the upper, outermost layer of soil – often recognized as the top two inches. This veil of life force is composed of air, mineral particles, organic matter and water. This mantle of topsoil is vital for all life on the planet and contains apical amounts of microorganisms and organic matter needed for the continuity of the circle of life. Most of the biological activity on Earth ensues in this bed of soil.

The complexity of soil will remain a miracle of nature until this resource becomes barren of the life force within. Herbicides and pesticides are slowly poisoning every molecule of life on this planet. Soil is eroding at an advanced pace. Fungi, insects and microorganisms – which make up the life force within soil – are going extinct from the saturation of chemicals in pesticides and herbicides. A single application of glyphosate alone can wipe out half of the earthworms in soil.

On *World Soil Day* the United Nations *Food and Agricultural Organization* (FAO) announced that generating three centimeters of topsoil takes one-thousand years and if current rates of degradation persist all of the world's topsoil could be gone in sixty years. A spokesperson for the UN FAO, Maria Helena-Semedo, declared: *Soils are the basis of life. Ninety-five percent of our food comes from soil. We are losing thirty soccer fields of soil every minute, mostly due to intensive farming (111).*

The intensive farming Maria speaks of is farming that requires the spraying of harmful pesticides and uses seeds that have been genetically modified to grow a single crop on large plots of land. This GMO monocropping is contributing to the

Jacoby

depletion of Earth's soil resources faster than her nutrients can be replenished. Healthy soil is needed to absorb and store carbon, nourish and provide foundation for crops, and filter water. Sequestration is the long-term storage of carbon in soil. As land is tilled and topsoil is depleted, carbon is released into the environment. Over two-thousand gigatons of carbon are stored in the top three meters of Earth's soil. This is a larger amount than is stored in all plants and the atmosphere combined. The area of land that has been used worldwide for farming has already released close to seventy gigatons of carbon into the atmosphere. One gigaton equates to one billion tons. Without soil nearly all living species would collapse and go extinct.

A May 2015 *Science* journal study (112) assessed at *University of Berkeley in California* deemed the supply of fertilizer as one of the key threats to future soil security. Most fertilizers are a combination of three nutrients – being nitrogen, phosphorus and potassium. Using permaculture methods of growing food we are able to regenerate soil without the use of fertilizers and chemical sprays, and also provide a more complete, diverse spectrum of nutrients.

We can learn from Native American wisdom how to farm and manage land sustainably. The Zuni tribe in the Southwestern United States uses a runoff agroecosystem that does not rely on conventional fertilization, irrigation, or pesticides. Their fields are identified as the oldest remaining in the United States. For centuries they have maintained soil fertility without direct fertilizer application. Their wisdom, and knowledge of the soil, are both vital when constructing a new agricultural paradigm.

With demands for dairy, eggs and meat continuing to increase yearly, rates of desertification and soil scarification also rise. The global amount of arable and productive land for farming, per person, in 2050 is estimated to be one-quarter of the level available in 1960. This decline also correlates with the increased application of glyphosate and other pesticides.

Today is the day to stop supporting conventional, intensive agriculture and shift to buying organic. This will extend your longevity, enrich soils, and purify air and water.

Fluctuations In Atmosphere Composition

In 2019 *Harvard University's School of Engineering and Applied Sciences* unveiled a plan, known as SCOPEX (113), to attempt to reduce carbon levels in the atmosphere using solar geoengineering. The idea is to spray sulfur aerosols into the upper atmosphere from jet planes that would somehow reflect sunlight and thereby reverse global warming. Their aim is to offset rising atmospheric CO2 levels using aluminum, barium and strontium oxides. This desperate attempt has been ongoing for decades and has never worked. These cloud-seeding programs and geothermal engineering techniques have changed weather patterns, inhibited rainfall and morphed the natural ecosystem in many regions. Additionally, high aluminum levels are found in the air, snow, soil and water beneath areas where they are spraying.

An October 2009 study published in *Atmospheric Environment* journal (114) notes how emissions of pollutants changes the atmospheric composition contributing to climate change. We learn that since the rise of oxygen two billion years ago, nitrogen and oxygen fractions in the atmosphere have been stable. Since the introduction of factory farms and feedlots there have been dramatic changes in carbon dioxide and methane levels in the atmosphere. This alters Earth's axis of rotation, orbit and volcanic activity.

Methane is released naturally in small amounts in freshwater, oceans, wetlands and through termites. Humans however, are responsible for two-thirds of the methane released into the atmosphere. The activities causing this pollution are livestock farming, biomass burning, landfills, rice paddies, coal mining, and gas production. Rather than spending outrageous amounts of money on geoengineering to spray metals into the environment we can simply stop eating animals and shift away from fossil fuels to save the climate.

"We aspire to possess less thunder in the mouth, and more lightning in the hands." – Apache prayer

Smoke Is Our Enemy

Before man, smoke was a rarity on Earth. When fires would burn, the strength of the forest canopy would use might to extinguish the flames. Strong Earthen winds alleviated our atmosphere of pollution and enriched the environment with caressing energy. With the global thinning of Earth's forests she is no longer able to protect these ecosystems from fires started by man. Wildfires do not exist. All fires that grow out of control are manmade. Logging companies, ranchers, and other businesses who need land intentionally ignite these fires every year to create work for their employees and expand the range of forests which they are permitted to cut down. This smoke permanently damages the health of animals who inhabit the surrounding land and causes long-lasting damage to the biosphere.

This year in the Amazon region of Brazil, and extending into Bolivia, there have already been over seventy-thousand fires started intentionally to clear land for agribusinesses. Over ninety percent of the deforestation is directly related to animal agriculture. Soy plantations are displacing trees and forests, and the soy is used as feed to fatten livestock. Humankind's addiction to beef is driving life on this planet to extinction. In major cities the skies have turned black from the smoke. Somewhere in the haze, the ghost of Chico Mendes is shaking his head.

A 2017 NASA study (115) conducted at *Georgia Institute of Technology* found that *brown carbon particles released into the air from burning trees and other organic matter travel to upper levels of the atmosphere and interfere with rays from the sun. This has a disproportionately large effect on the planetary radiation balance. Brown carbon is found in the upper troposphere seven miles above Earth's surface. Black carbon is found in dark smoke plumes rising above burning fossil or biomass fuels at high temperature.* The combination of black and brown carbon is causing irreversible damage to the atmosphere.

When I was younger I had a native Choctaw elder, Pushmataha, visit me in a plant-medicine ceremony. He spoke to me with a familiar voice that echoed my father's. He said, *"My son, great turtle showed me when I was transitioning from this life how we made a fatal error when our land was invaded by settlers. We were never intended to kill the bison or salmon for our own survival. Never are we to take another life to enrich our own. We were mistaken to have shown the white man how to hunt the bison for food. This inflicted our heritage and race with a karmic wound that ended in genocide and massacre of not only our people, but the vast population of buffalo."*

He continued to tell me that his only regret in life was that he did not listen to the land. He failed to utilize the diverse range of fruits, grains and vegetables to sustain his health and instead cheated the animals of their lives. If there was one lesson he believed we all should live in accordance to, he pleaded, the lesson would be not to ever inflict pain or suffering on any other living beings. Before his visit was up, he added, *Our defense against the white man was the plague of tobacco addiction. We used the sacred tobacco ceremonially to connect with spirit, but we never inhaled this toxic smoke. Our revenge was teaching these men to inhale the smoke into their lungs. As they brutally raped, dismembered and tortured our people, their health also began to decline from the smoke.*

Millions of people around the world today die each year from health issues related to tobacco smoke, and millions more begin smoking tobacco for no purpose other than to shorten their lifespan and contribute to the degradation of Earth. There is nothing more ignorant and unnecessary than smoking cigarettes. A November 2016 *National Institute of Health* study (116) found that smoking a pack a day of cigarettes causes one-hundred fifty cellular mutations in lungs, ninety-seven mutations in cells of the larynx, and thirty-nine mutations in cells of the pharynx (throat).

If we want to restore our health, we need to detach from smoke. All diverse life forms on this planet are sensitive to smoke and pollutants from smoke. As we learn to coexist with other forms of life and come back to our senses we also inherit an innate sense of protecting ourselves from what ails us and everything around us. Please choose this day to give up your addiction to what makes less of you.

"Smoking is the leading cause of statistics."

Freshwater Depletion

"Globalization of natural resources like ancient forests undermines the stability of our watersheds and communities. In order to achieve true sustainability for all life forms we must put our primary needs of fresh air, clean water and biological and cultural diversity above corporate profits." – Julia Butterfly Hill, *Legacy of Luna*

Many areas in the United States are experiencing groundwater depletion. These long-term water-level declines are caused by groundwater pumping for sustaining the dairy, egg, meat and wine industries. When various farms these industries are composed of pump groundwater faster than can be recharged – especially during times of drought – the result is freshwater depletion. This excessive and irresponsible use of water for egregious agricultural practices lowers water tables, deteriorates water quality, dries up wells and also reduces levels of water in lakes and streams. Many creeks, lakes, rivers and streams dry up completely during seasons of no rain. Without animal agriculture and wineries we would not witness this depletion of our most precious resource.

Drawing from the *National Geographic water footprint calculator,* 880 gallons of water are used in the process of producing one gallon of milk. The *Water Education Foundation* indicates for every pound of beef produced, 2,464 gallons of water are used (117). The *GRACE Communications Foundation* (118) calculated that fifty-three gallons of water are needed for each egg – over six-hundred gallons per dozen. Each year in California alone factory farms are using 4,705,954,400,000 gallons of water to produce milk and meat products. This is close to five trillion gallons of water.

Larry Williams, a professor in the *Department of Viticulture and Enology* at *UC Davis*, conducted research on grapevines and wineries to determine how much water is required for a glass of wine. His findings inform us that up to fourteen gallons of water are used for each four ounce glass of wine (119).

Native American tribes believe running water is a symbol of continuity of life. Those enrolled in the ideologies of Western culture believe running water needs to be controlled with dams, polluted with chemicals, and bottled for profit. Fifty-five percent of all freshwater flow is usurped and diverted for profitable agendas by humans. Researchers predict by 2025 as much as two-thirds of the world population will be living in conditions of serious water shortage. Thirty-one countries face serious water scarcity and more than one-billion people lack adequate access to drinking water. In these same regions livestock never go thirsty. When an aquifer drops a meter a year and takes in salt water, this water source is lost forever.

Finding pure water today is growing increasingly difficult. Animal excrement from factory farms and feedlots seeps into every aquifer. This devastation, paired with the dangerous cocktails used for fracking and the coal ash dumped from mountaintop removal, formulates a toxic brew. Glyphosate has made home of our water reserves. The great lakes and Mississippi River are gradually becoming cesspools of glyphosate waste. This chemical is penetrating every water source. To metabolize glyphosate, algae forms. With the decomposition of algae, depleted oxygen levels create ocean and freshwater dead zones.

Government systems all around the world are stripping environmental legislation and allowing the bottled water industry to govern water economics. Multinational corporations enslave water as a private commodity and sell and trade this precious resource on the open market. This cannot be tolerated. These same government regimes and corporations that poison nearly every source of water are not to control and dictate this source of life.

If we want clean water we must make the decision to stop supporting the industries responsible for depleting and contaminating water. This includes refusing to buy bottled waters from corporations that are funneling water into bottles and choosing not to ingest dairy, eggs, meat or wine. We need to be more mindful of where water is being used and how much our everyday choices impact this resource.

The Last Drop – Water Fluoridation

"The sad irony here is that the FDA, which does not regulate fluoride in drinking water, does regulate toothpaste. The back of a tube of fluoridated toothpaste states, 'If your child swallows more than the recommended amount, contact a poison control center.' The recommended amount that they are talking about, which is a pea-sized amount, is equivalent to one glass of fluoridated tap water. The FDA is not putting a label on the tap saying, 'Do not drink more than one glass of water. If you do, contact a poison center.' There is no question that fluoride can cause serious harm." – Paul Connett, *The Case Against Fluoride*

Fluoride – in the form of sodium fluoride, fluorosilicic acid or sodium fluorosilicate – is added to seventy-five percent of municipal water systems in the United States. This substance is not allowed to be dumped in landfills because of the high level of toxicity, yet is added to infant drinking water. Much of the fluoride used for water fluoridation is recovered from phosphoric acid plants or as a byproduct from the manufacturing of aluminum and war weapons. Although a growing number of scientific studies suggest consumption of fluoride poses a human health risk, much of the water supply is still being saturated with this chemical. Most fluoride added to municipal water is an unnatural form of fluoride that contains sodium. Sodium fluoride is over eighty times more toxic than naturally-occurring calcium fluoride. This is one of the most deadly chemicals there is. The *Material Data Safety Sheet* (MSDS) for sodium fluoride shows the lethal dose (LD-50) that will kill fifty percent of a population of rats is 52 mg/kg. The LD-50 for calcium fluoride is 4250 mg/kg (120). Many people are exposed to this chemical each time they wash their hands, clean dishes and shower or bathe.

A November 2010 review published in *Chemico-Biological Interactions* (121) points out how consumption of fluoride interferes with numerous enzymes and is associated with arthritis, hip fractures, impaired kidney function, lowered IQ, and skeletal fluorosis. Over one-hundred animal studies demonstrate how fluoride causes brain damage and impacts learning and behavior. Thirty-three human studies show association between exposure to this chemical and reduced IQ. An adult considered to be healthy is able to excrete up to sixty percent of ingested fluoride daily through the kidneys. The remaining accumulates in calcifying tissues such as bones, joints and the pineal gland. Infants and children are unable to process fluoride as effectively as adults and absorb up to eighty percent of this substance into their bones.

Calcification of the pineal gland is caused by drinking water contaminated with chemicals and eating combinations of pharmaceutical drugs, farming chemical residues and chemical food additives. When the pineal gland is blocked we no longer generate sufficient amounts of melatonin. This hormone keeps us happy and elevates harmony. A lack of melatonin can dull senses, lower intellect, make us feel sluggish and drain our desire to achieve more in life.

Dr. James Sumner won a Nobel prize in the 1950s for his research on enzymes. He once explained how fluoride is used in enzyme chemistry to poison and kill enzymes. To euthanize animals and plants in experiments he would proceed to kill the enzymes first. In humans fluoride inhibits production of several important detoxification enzymes, leading to inevitable sickness. Of these enzymes, catalase and cytochrome P450 are of notable importance. We need these enzymes for detoxifying heavy metals from our body. Aluminum and glyphosate are also known to inhibit these enzymes.

In August 2019 a trial date is set to decide on a lawsuit filed by six different entities opposed to water fluoridation against the *Environmental Protection Agency* to ban water fluoridation. Until a safe ban is in place do your best to install a reverse osmosis water filter in your home. In addition, be sure to place filters on your faucets and shower heads. When you drink water always avoid tap water and bottled waters. The safest water to drink is distilled, followed by reverse osmosis.

Redwoods, Not Grapes – Saving Forests From Wineries

There are hundreds of thousands of acres of grapevines littering the bulldozed remains of what were once ancient redwood forests in the Northwest Pacific region of the United States. A lot of people think of Sonoma County and associate this land with wineries. Grapevines are actually invasive to this region. Before alcoholism and the lies about wine being healthy plagued humanity this land was lush with beautiful redwood forests. Now all we see are ugly grapevines that are sprayed with chemicals daily. Trading forests for alcohol is the epitome of ignorance. Each drop of wine contains the moral tears of bobcats, mountain lions, ravens and owls; the ashes of ancient redwood roots and trees; ground up remains of mosses and soil microorganisms; and the poison that slowly ages and degenerates the human body.

Creeks and streams around wineries dry up unusually early in the season because of the high water demand from these vines. A typical modern spacing of four feet by seven feet will allot for fifteen hundred grapevines per acre. Each vine requires roughly ten gallons of water per day. This equates to each acre commanding fifteen thousand gallons of water on a daily basis. According to *World Atlas*, there are *well over eighteen million acres of cultivated vineyards worldwide (122)*. These calculations inform us that the world expends 270 million gallons of water daily for sustaining the wine industry.

Grapes are sprayed relentlessly with harmful chemicals that include carbaryl, esfenvalerate, spinosad, permethrin, malathion and pyrethrin. These health-depleting compounds affix to grapes and are pressed into wine. Humans eventually ingest them in each glass they consume. Additionally, glyphosate drifts and is found in all wines that are produced in the state of California. A supporter of the advocacy group, *Moms Across America*, sent wine samples to a lab to be tested for glyphosate. Every sample tested positive (123).

While grapevines are not directly sprayed with glyphosate, the chemical still integrates into the grapevine because the ground area on both sides of the vine is often sprayed. When speaking at the *Acres USA farm conference* in December 2011, Dr. Don Huber explained how *vine stems are inevitably sprayed during this process.* As a result, *glyphosate is absorbed through the roots and bark of the vines from where the compound is translocated into the leaves and grapes.* This reveals how wines that are labeled as organic are still contaminated with this herbicide.

While lobbyists for the wine industry have advocated for many years that wine is health-promoting, several studies contradict these claims. A 2018 *Journal of Neuroinflammation* study *(124)* found that wine consumption can interrupt the body's natural ability to clear amyloid plaque from the brain – thus leading to Alzheimer's and dementia. Results from this study show how the brain naturally removes these plaques through the glymphatic system which consists of cells known as activated microglial cells. When this system functions adequately, the amyloid is cleansed through the blood and lymphatic fluids. The research team discovered that alcohol consumption causes the microglial cells to become inflamed and cease to function. This leads to a gradual buildup of amyloid plaque that is positively associated with cognitive decline.

In addition, a March 2019 *BMC Public Health* journal study (125) used a comparative risk analysis study to determine that the increase in cancer risk associated with drinking one bottle of wine per week is equivalent to smoking five cigarettes per week for men, and ten cigarettes per week for women. Wine consumption has been a known carcinogen for many years, yet the widespread belief still remains that this drink is somehow beneficial for health. Truth is, wine is not required for good health and is only detrimental.

If we seek antioxidants from grapes, we can simply eat grapes. There are several antioxidants equally as effective as resveratrol for combating free radicals in the body. I like to eat blueberries and cherries for antioxidants. I also add acai and camu camu berry powder to my smoothies.

A Timed Mine

I am a guided missile.
My target is human consciousness.

I have been launched to blow apart the current paradigm that locks our minds in confinement.

I am a timed mine, awaiting detonation.
A bomb that is ticking for the evolution of understanding.

I am the virus that will heal this nation from the plague of profitable devastation.
A vaccine that protects us from the disease called separation.
Biological warfare spreading unification.

I am a military tank on a mission to plow down prison walls and free armies of imprisoned potential from the court system's stronghold – to provide redemption.

I am a grenade.
When my pin is pulled all violence will implode.
From my ashes peace will resurrect and wars will fall.

I am a brandished pistol.
In my chamber are bullets of love that will inflict wounds of happiness on heavy hearts.

I am a syringe dripping with the medicine of clarity that is the anti-drug.
An elixir that will kill the ego and wipe out the lust for riches.

I am a soldier in the infantry of awareness sent to save this civilization from arrogance.

I am an artillery firing munitions of smiling faces.

A nuclear weapon that will free us all from our cages.

I am a cannonball shooting to expel hatred.

Watch out world, my desire is contagious.

Single Largest Polluter – Animal Agriculture

"The act of regularly eating foods derived from confined and brutalized animals forces us to become somewhat emotionally desensitized, and this numbing and inner armoring opens the possibility for us as a culture to devastate the earth, slaughter people in wars and support oppressive social structures without feeling remorse. By going vegan, we are taking responsibility for the effects of our actions on vulnerable beings and resensitizing ourselves. We are becoming more alive and more able to feel both grief and joy." – Will Tuttle, PhD, *The World Peace Diet*

Raising animals for food uses more water than any other method of agriculture. According to the *U.S. Department of Agriculture's Census of Agriculture* there are 1.7 million dairy cows, 563,000 beef cattle, 131,000 hogs, 49.6 million broiler chickens and 19.7 million egg-laying hens on factory farms in California. The amount of water being used to raise these animals is seriously draining water aquifers and reservoirs.

Drawing from the *National Geographic* water footprint calculator, 880 gallons of water are used in the process of producing one gallon of milk. The *Midwest Dairy Association* reports the average dairy cow produces up to seven gallons of milk daily (126). This informs us each dairy cow is using 6,160 gallons of water daily to produce seven gallons of milk. We are essentially throwing away 6,153 gallons of water for every seven gallons of milk we consume. With 1.7 million dairy cows on factory farms in the state consuming water at a rate of 6,160 gallons per cow per day, we are diverting 10,472,000,000 gallons of water per day to milk production. This comes out to an annual water usage of 3,822,280,000,000 gallons in the state of California simply so we can drink the milk of another species not designed for us to consume. Close to four trillion gallons of water each year are being wasted to manufacture a product that is known to promote breast and prostate cancer, diabetes, heart disease, osteoporosis, and obesity.

The *Water Education Foundation* indicates for every pound of beef produced 2,464 gallons of water are used. This is also a generous number. Several other reports claim more water is used per pound. For every pound of pork produced 1,630 gallons of water are needed and for every pound of chicken up to 815 gallons are used. The *Oklahoma Department of Agriculture* declares the average one-thousand pound steer will produce around four-hundred forty pounds of retail beef cuts, and the average two-hundred fifty pound hog will produce around 144 pounds of retail pork cuts. The target weight for a boiler chicken is six pounds. Using these numbers as a base we can determine how much water is being used annually for the production of factory-farmed beef, chicken and pork in the state of California. The 563,000 cattle alone will produce up to 247,720,000 pounds of beef. Using 2,464 gallons of water to manufacture each pound we realize 610,382,080,000 gallons are being used annually in California to produce factory-farmed beef. This is over six-hundred billion gallons of water.

According to David Pimentel, *Professor of Ecology and Agricultural Science* at *Cornell University, we could go two years without a shower and still not save as much water as we would by not eating one pound of beef (127).* From the 131,000 hogs in factory farms 18,864,000 pounds of pork will be produced. At 1,630 gallons of water per pound this requires 30,748,320,000 gallons. This is over thirty billion gallons of water. Finally, from the 49.6 million boiler chickens in factory farms at six pounds per chicken, we are looking at 297,600,000 pounds of chicken meat produced. With each pound requiring up to 815 gallons of water the total annual water usage comes to 242,544,000,000 gallons.

Judging by the amount of water being wasted to produce milk, beef, pork and chicken for human consumption we can admit we are mistaken in our common widespread philosophy regarding food sustainably. There is absolutely nothing sustainable about eating meat or drinking milk and there is most definitely a dire need to end the dangerous practice of factory farming.

Each year in California alone factory farms are using 4,705,954,400,000 gallons of water to produce milk and meat products. This is close to five trillion gallons of water. To understand this better think about how much water is used to produce one pound of apples, carrots, kale, potatoes, quinoa and tomatoes. To produce one pound of each of these crops, and a total of six pounds of food, requires a total of less than two-hundred gallons of water. You also provide your body with more nourishment by eating this variety of foods than you would from consuming animal products. Can you imagine how plentiful our most precious resource – water – would be if we simply refrained from allowing factory farms to operate?

The EPA estimates each household uses about three-hundred gallons of water per day. According to the *U.S Census Bureau* there was a population total of 38,322,521 in California in 2013. This means for the entire population of California we would need 11,499,756,300 gallons of water a day to sustain life and 4,197,411,049,500 gallons annually. This is almost equivalent to the amount of water being used for producing milk and meat in the state alone. By placing a permanent ban on factory farming corporations may lose profits, however we will create a surplus of water, open job opportunities on fruit and vegetable farms and drastically reduce greenhouse gas emissions.

The perverse idea that animals should be raised for food and sadistic practice of confining them in factory farms, or on feedlots with no purpose other than fattening for slaughter, is piercing the karmic wound man is afflicted by and plastering enemy to our identity. The mass breeding; exploitation of land and other resources; immoral and unethical treatment of sentient beings; emissions of greenhouse gases; antibiotic injections; overproduction of excrement; and environmental travesties associated with animal agriculture are responsible for the extinction of cultures and species all over the world; heartbreaking rises in deforestation; pollution of air, soil and water; and our chances of escaping the sixth mass extinction nearing the level of impossible.

According to a 2018 Oxford study published in *Science* journal *(128)*, animal agriculture uses about eighty-three percent of global farmland but only provides eighteen percent of calories. Lead researcher, Joseph Poore, reported that *with current diets and production practices, feeding 7.6 billion people is degrading terrestrial and aquatic ecosystems, depleting water resources and driving climate change.* Food production was found to create thirty-two percent of global terrestrial acidification and seventy-eight percent of eutrophication.

Emissions from animal agriculture are known to *fundamentally alter the species composition of natural ecosystems thereby reducing biodiversity and ecological resilience.* The study findings indicate that replacing meat and dairy with plant-based farming would reduce global farmland use by seventy-five percent and could still provide enough food to feed everyone in the world.

There are close to seventy billion farm animals alive every moment. Most are locked in tiny cages being raised to die with no love, nourishment or nurturing. Nature would never produce this many chickens, cows or pigs. The thought is irrational. Prevalence of disease is directly proportioned with the overproduction of farm animals. Humans are annihilating ecological balance and creating incongruities within their own health and well-being by choosing to confide in the unnatural.

There is no denying the environmental impact eating animals and their by-products has on the planet. With billions of animals being raised in cages, forced to eat chemically saturated GMO feed and being poisoned with antibiotics, we have to question where all of the feces end up, where they are getting the feed, and where they are finding land to raise these animals. On the *EarthSave* website (*earthsave.org*), we see one-half of Earth's landmass is grazed by livestock. This makes half of all land unlivable for humans or wildlife. We also learn over seventy percent of all U.S. grain production is fed to livestock.

For those who worry about carbon dioxide emissions from humans, a more imminent threat is the enormous population of caged farm animals also emitting greenhouse gases in much larger quantities. We may be surprised to learn of the rainforests all around the world being destroyed to clear land for growing GMO alfalfa, corn, soy and wheat – which is used as feed for livestock. Ranchers and GMO soy farmers are being instructed by the Government to intentionally start fires all over the region. More forests are being decimated for factory farms and cattle ranches. Do you realize up to five million pounds of animal excrement are produced every minute in the United States alone in factory farms? This is confirmed in *Livestock's Long Shadow (129)*, a 2009 *United Nations* report released by the *Food and Agriculture Organization*. With this excrement comes methane gases and excess nitrogen. This animal waste is dumped in our lakes, oceans, rivers and streams leading to ocean dead zones and habitat destruction for many wild animals. Methane gases, nitrous oxide and carbon being emitted from the mass breeding of farm animals, clear cutting of forests and animal excrement is the number one contributor to global warming – responsible for over fifty-one percent of all greenhouse gas emissions.

Millions of pounds of animal excrement are produced every minute in the United States alone. This equates to three-hundred million pounds per hour and 7.2 billion pounds each day. Calculations reveal there are 2.6 trillion pounds of animal feces produced every year in the United States. This is an environmental disaster. The end of the human species will be the result of asphyxiation from choking on gases released from the excess of manure from jailed farm animals on factory farms and feedlots, and the contamination of the water supply with these animal feces. Mankind will literally *eat shit and die*. This is devastating and could so easily be reversed if we would all collectively agree to relinquish the habit of eating animals and transition to plant-based diets.

"Clean air, water, and a livable climate are inalienable human rights. Solving this crisis is not a question of politics, but a question of our own survival." – Leonardo DiCaprio

Jailed Farm Animals

"Believe me, every morsel of meat you eat is slapping the tear-stained, hungry face of a starving child." – Philip Wollen

The 2017 *USDA Census of Agriculture* reported a total of 1,229,542 animal farming operations for chickens, cows, egg-laying hens, pigs and turkeys in the United States. On these farms there are a total of over ten billion animals locked in confinement. These beautiful species are forbidden from receiving fresh air, feeling the warmth of sunlight and having the ability to extend their limbs or flap their wings. They become products on an assembly line. USDA statistics indicate a total of 32,751 chicken farms housing around nine billion chickens; 232,500 egg-laying hen farms containing over 368 million hens; 11,154 turkey farms compacted with over 285 million turkeys; 66,439 pig farms enslaving over seventy-two million pigs and 886,692 cow farms imprisoning over ninety-five million cows.

In 1950 there were over five million farms raising around one-hundred million animals. In 2017 that number decreased to two million farms, yet these farms now raise over nine billion farm animals. This practice of raising as much livestock as possible in as small of a space as they can is elevating profits for agribusinesses at the cost of millions of tons of manure and toxic pollutants for the rest of the world to process. Using data from the USDA census, an estimated seventy percent of cows, ninety-eight percent of pigs, ninety-nine percent of turkeys, ninety-eight percent of chickens raised for eggs and ninety-nine percent of chickens raised for meat are confined in factory farms. According to *Statista (130)* there were just over two million farms in the United States in 2018. This country produced over two-hundred and seventeen billion pounds of milk from cows for human consumption, fifty-three billion pounds of red meat and six billion pounds of turkey in 2018. In addition, global cattle population was just short of one billion last year. Sadly, around twenty-one percent of all this meat manufactured and purchased is thrown away and wasted. This equates to billions of animals being killed for no reason.

Intensive factory farming threatens the environment and human health to a larger degree than any other factor around the globe. The widespread loss of biodiversity from soil and water acidification associated with factory farming is intolerable. Water eutrophication from the discharge of nitrates in animal manure and the overload of phosphate-containing fertilizers, herbicides and pesticides applied to animal feed dissolves the purity and cleanliness we need to acquire optimal health. Reduced soil fertility, increased salinity of freshwater and desertification of what was once arable land is all attributed to farming animals. There has never been a practice adapted by man that is more destructive than raising animals for food. Livestock related habitat destruction causes extinction of species all over the world and is the number one cause of extinction of plants. Tens of millions of blackbirds and starlings are poisoned simply to keep them from eating animal feed. Every aspect of animal agriculture is in complete defiance of nature and the circle of life.

Non-point source pollution (131) can be described as the transfer of pollutants into coastal and ground waters, lakes, rivers and wetlands from rainfall or snowmelt as the water moves over and through the ground. The *National Water Quality Assessment (132)* shows that agricultural non-point source pollution is the leading source of water quality impacts on surveyed rivers and streams, third largest source for lakes, second largest source of impairments to wetlands and a major contributor to contamination of surveyed estuaries and ground water. This pollution is a result of animal feeding operations and their improper application of fertilizer, irresponsible plowing, overgrazing, and overload of manure produced. Every year when the snow melts and heavy rains bless the land with water the toxins generated from factory farms and farming chemicals used to produce animal feed are moved to the waterways – spreading poison to every region of the world. We can no longer support this ecocidal intrusion.

The EPA claims cattle, chicken and hog waste has polluted thirty-five thousand miles of rivers throughout twenty-two states in the United States and permanently contaminated groundwater in seventeen states. According to their *Toxic Release Inventory (133)*, the five major agribusinesses that are responsible for factory farming operations in the United States – Cargill, JBS, Purdue, Smithfield and Tyson – produce close to one-hundred and sixty-three million tons of manure on average yearly. Tyson alone dumped over one-hundred million pounds of pollutants into United States waterways between the years 2010 and 2014. Much of this pollution is from nitrate compounds in animal waste. When exposed to this pollutant, nitrate is known to hinder man's ability to carry oxygen to cells, leading to severe health problems. In waterways these nitrates cause algal blooms which lead to ocean dead zones. The largest factory farms produced around three-hundred sixty-nine million tons of feces in 2012. This is thirteen times more than the entire human population and would fill a whole football stadium one-hundred and thirty-three times.

The *National Association of Local Boards of Health (134)* reports that 1.37 billion tons of waste are produced each year raising livestock. Chicken farming in Maryland alone produces six-hundred and fifty million pounds of manure annually. Raising animals for food is the number one source of water pollution – causing more pollution than all other industrial sources combined. The meat industry is also responsible for eighty-five percent of all soil erosion in the United States. For as long as mankind continues to imprison, abuse and slaughter animals for the food supply there will be disharmony, poor health and pollution. This planet will not be able to sustain such deleterious and egregious methods of satiating hunger for much longer.

We need to establish a new *Environmental Protection Agency* that actually protects the environment if we wish to change these trends. The EPA in place today is governed by industries responsible for devastating the planet. Never should an agency expected to protect the environment be allowing toxic release of any kind, yet alone be keeping inventory each year of how frequently and to what extent corporations are polluting.

Drowning In Animal Feces

Future generations will look back at the way society was governed today and likely be dumbfounded by the stupidity of mankind. How could a species blessed with such vast intelligence be ignorant enough to kill themselves and harm every other species on the planet by continuing to eat the wrong foods and spray health-degrading chemicals everywhere persistently for so long? By refusing to transition away from eating animals toward adapting a sustainable plant-centered lifestyle, the entire planet is being poisoned with the excrement of farm animals.

A single dairy cow produces one-hundred and twenty pounds of wet manure per day – equivalent to the feces produced by up to forty humans (135). The 1.8 million dairy cows in California are responsible for generating as much excrement as nearly seventy-two million people. In fact, farm animals produce one-hundred and thirty times more waste than all humans combined. Every second roughly eighty-nine thousand pounds of waste pile up in factory farms across the United States.

Animal waste emits ammonia, hydrogen sulfite, methane, particulate matter from fecal dust and various volatile organic compounds – each attributed to mood disorders and respiratory disease. The *Center for Disease Control and Prevention (CDC)* admits that chemical infectious compounds from swine and poultry waste migrate into soil and water. More than forty diseases can be transferred to humans through manure polluted waterways. Ammonia that is generated during waste disposal can be carried more than three-hundred miles through the air before dissipating into water sources. The pollution strength of raw manure is found to be up to one-hundred and sixty times stronger than raw municipal sewage. Much of the waste collected in animal feeding operations is either stored in brown lagoons or sprayed onto fields. To circumvent pollution limits, when cesspools of feces and urine are filled to capacity, farmers spray liquid manure into the air that spreads mists for miles. This contaminates the air we breathe with pathogens and toxins. Those living nearby inhale this poison into their lung tissues.

Unusually high rates of depression and anxiety are common among people who live near factory farms. Breathing in these particulates can alter mood and cause feelings of anger and anguish. Nitrate levels in water also elevate as a result of feces from animal farms leaching into the estuaries, rivers and streams. A *United States Geological Survey* from *Oklahoma Department of Agriculture* (136) found that ingesting water with nitrate levels above ten milligrams per liter causes *blue baby syndrome.* This is a condition that prevents blood from carrying oxygen. This can be attributed to birth defects, leukemia, lymphoma, miscarriages and several other cancers.

Breathing in the manure mist and drinking water contaminated with nitrates stagnates the lymphatic system. When lymphatic cells are not regenerated efficiently and lymphatic fluid is blocked from flowing, health issues arise. Dr. Kaye Kilburn, a University of Southern California toxicology professor, explains how *the coincidence of people showing a pattern of impairment and being exposed to hydrogen sulfide arising from lagoons where hog manure is stored and sprayed onto fields or in the air has a practically undeniable connection to neurological disorders in communities around farms (137).*

We need a collective awakening for this to stop. For as long as one person continues to eat meat and support animal agriculture many more will join them. The entire fallacy of ingesting dead animals for nourishment must be abolished. We can no longer poison the air, soil and waterways with this astounding amount of animal waste. A sustainable approach to sufficing the dietary needs of a growing population needs to be drafted and implemented as global policy immediately. The simplest, most environmentally-friendly and prosperous approach to accomplishing this starts with a plant-based diet.

"Pig farms in North Carolina produce so much waste that the ground water reserves of the entire state are contaminated. Citizens drink pig feces with their water but assume they are safe because the waste is neutralized with chlorine." – Captain Paul Watson, *Sea Shepherd*

A Human Parasite – Finding Mankind Among Evil

I am suffering from a disease called civilization.

I keep choking on plastic that saturates the oceans.

I have been experiencing chronic malabsorption of knowledge because education and information provided by school systems, textbooks, and mainstream media outlets fails to satiate my hungry mind.

I was afflicted with a mental illness called deforestation.

I am constipated with indigenous genocide.

My pineal gland is calcified with chemicals and poisons that are being ingested in the food and water supply and linger in the soil.

I was diagnosed as being anemic to damning rivers.

I suffocate inside of factory farms breathing in pain, torture, rape, and murder.

My lungs are cracking from second-hand smoke, orangutan and palm tree ashes, and animal agriculture's greenhouse gases.

I am dyslexic from prescription pills that sedate me from finding my purpose.

Brain-dead from watching television lies and being bribed by mistruths.

Cancer eats at me in school cafeterias, fast food restaurants, processed foods, milk cartons, and barbecues.

My skin is eroding from fracking wells, tar sands, and oil drills.

My eyes are partially blind because what society is showing me is not a part of my vision.

I am a parasite known as a human.

My host is a beautiful planet called Earth.

Similar to how parasites can infiltrate the human body and wreak havoc on our organs, humanity has become parasitic to Earth. Rather than acting as harmful organisms however, we can play the role of beneficial bacteria. Collectively we can overpower and expel harmful activities on the planet, and just like probiotics do with disruptive bacteria, we can eliminate the evil dominating the world.

Mankind echoes the cries of a planet in peril. We are a species incoherent of the permanence of our destruction. As we emit exhalations of methane and abhorrence, we display elements of dysfunction. We poison for profit, shoot up infants with deadly cocktails and act as if we are Godless. Hygienal products are laced with cancerous compounds. Tampons and douches taint the wombs of girls. Deodorants and lotions slow the function of organs. Colognes and perfumes paralyze alveoli. The chemicals added to food are feeding parasites that have commandeered human consciousness. Lawn fertilizers, weed killers, insect control – these are all devastating human health and insect populations.

People suck sugary fluoride drinks through plastic straws and their guts are rotting. The meat they ingest degrades health and their immunity is perishing. Fluoride and pharmaceuticals have rewired their brains so they appear as being careless. Beneath these crowns of shame corporations have plastered around their brains, this human race is capable of changing face. Without the poison that drowns out alertness mankind can end the hurting. Doses of encouragement will help them recognize their worth and establish purpose. We are what Earth needs to regenerate.

"Many of us consume in a way that is very violent. Forests are cut down to raise cattle for beef, or to grow grain for liquor, while millions in the world are dying of starvation. Eating with compassion can already help transform the situation our planet is facing, and restore balance to ourselves and Earth." – Thich Nhat Hanh

End Cruelty – Animal Protection

"Only when we have truly fallen back in love with the Earth will our actions spring from reverence and the insight of our interconnectedness. Yet many of us have become alienated from Earth. We are lost, isolated and lonely. We work too hard, our lives are too busy, and we are restless and distracted, losing ourselves in consumption. But Earth is always there for us, offering us everything we need for our nourishment and healing: the miraculous grain of corn, refreshing stream, fragrant forest, majestic snow-capped mountain peak, and joyful birdsong at dawn." – Thich Nhat Hanh

Compassion is the ganglion and vital center of human goodness. There is no reason why at any moment we should ever display actions demonstrative of violence or an attitude effusive of animosity. Our intentions cannot ever be directed toward belittling any person or bringing their frequency to a lower level. Kindness, therefore is a virtue. This mercy and benevolence extends to all living entities.

Trees are living creatures with soul. Their sap is blood. Their roots are tendons and veins. They communicate just as we do. Animals feel pain identical to humans. From this perspective we can safely assert that eating meat and ingesting stomach filler derived from animals is immoral, unethical and barbaric.

While vegetables are also living, when we eat their fibrous consistency we are not killing the plant. The life force present is maintained in the nutrients and as we ingest, the nutrients transfer to our system where we use them to fuel life. In animals, once killed, the life force escapes and flesh begins to decompose. The nutrition becomes inadequate. This is why true carnivores only ingest prey they have chased down and inherit life from. They attack to extract the life force energy from their prey. When we consume animal flesh stripped of living energy we take on dead matter and this depletes our livelihood. Finding our center – rooted in compassion – deepens our sense of connection and understanding.

Jacoby

Protecting Wildlife

Loss of biodiversity haunts us similar to the sound of gunshots to an orphaned fawn. The reckless actions of mankind are insurmountable to the sustenance of life on this planet. All animal species are endangered. In the last century we are responsible for the decline of eighty-three percent of wild animals on land and eighty percent of marine mammals. Most of these irreplaceable animals on land are being driven to extinction to protect farm animals or from loss of habitat for the expansion of animal agriculture. To protect all species we need to nurture, love and coexist with wildlife.

The United States government has a sector known as the *United States Wildlife Services*. Those employed by this federal agency under the *Department of Agriculture* (USDA) are paid solely to kill wild animals. They snipe wolves and wild cats from helicopters, gas bears while they hibernate and sleep in their dens and set snares and traps for them to be wounded and killed. One of their methods for murder is to use the M-44 – a spring-loaded device that is planted in the ground and ejects sodium cyanide when set off. The focus for these government trappers is to protect livestock by killing predatory animals. These animals are native to the homeland, while cattle and other farm animals have been imported here and mass-bred by humans. There has never been a definition more fitting for cowardice. Taxpayer dollars are diverted toward funding this malicious program and until recently not a single person has acted to put an end to this barbarous practice.

The USDA reports (138) that this government program killed 2.6 million animals consisting of over a hundred species in 2018. This equates to around five animals per minute. They slaughter bears, beavers, birds, bobcats, coyotes, feral pigs, otters, prairie dogs, wolves, and several other species.

The greatest statement we can make, and course of action we can take to stop this, is to transition to veganism.

Play The Fool

Another sleepless night.
I cannot rest when cows and pigs are screaming,
being sentenced to death for no reason.

How can I close my eyes when theirs are wide open?
Watching their babies get stolen,
knowing their fate has been chosen.

Why are children expected to drink milk from animals being
raped, beaten and force-fed chemicals and poisons?

They are lied to and taught they need milk to strengthen their
bones when really all the product does is sicken them and
weaken their soul.

Meat does not make us strong, but acidifies our blood and is
morally wrong.

Animal flesh destroys our organs, fattens our bellies and
corrodes us.

For as long as the slaughterhouses produce what we call food
this will always be hell we live in.

There is no time left to play the fool.

Fisherman's Parody – Why Fishing Needs To End

A fisherman out at sea once awoke to his favorite breakfast meal bedside on a plate. He was delighted and did not think to question where the food came from. He instinctively took a bite. As he chewed, a hook penetrated his gums and pierced through his cheek tearing away at his face. He was soon thrust from his bed by a force pulling at the hook and dragged overboard into the sea. Beneath the surface of the sea he could not breathe. He choked, coughed and tried with all of his might to get above water so he could take in fresh air but was clubbed in the head with a large object and knocked unconscious. His life soon ended.

Similar to how humans are unable to breathe under water a fish undergoes an identical experience when removed from the water. Humans do not belong in the oceans and fish should never be pulled from water. Contrary to what school teaches, fish do have feelings and they are not inanimate objects. Fish have families, friends and loved ones. When we disregard their desire to live and take their life to eat their flesh we inflict karmic wounds against humanity.

People all over the world are suffering and their anguish is in direct proportion with the animals struggling to survive. As life in the sea is killed for what we think is seafood our vitality is also drained. There is an abundance of seafood in the oceans – algae, plankton and other sea plants. What humans eat is dead sea life.

A 2017 report by *Stimson Center* (139) found that up to ninety percent of fisheries in the world are over-exploited and depleted. For every pound of shrimp trawled in nets there are up to six pounds of by-catch on average. This includes dolphins, rays, sharks, turtles and whales as casualties. *Sea Shepherd* estimates that illegal fishing accounts for up to twenty-six million tons of annual catch of fish globally. Profits from these illegal catches equate to nearly thirty-six billion dollars. In addition, nine million tons of plastic end up in the ocean each year and this is attributed to the killing of one million sea birds and one-hundred thousand marine mammals. Captain Paul Watson declares that cows and domesticated house cats have become the largest ocean predators because the by-catch is ground up into animal feed.

Man's desire to domesticate animals and have feline kitties as pets, coupled with the extensive use of plastic, is responsible for much of the degradation and depletion of aquatic life. As lakes, oceans, rivers and streams continue to be over-fished, entire colonies and species of marine life perish – often being driven to extinction. Ocean dead zones expand. We create an overabundance of jelly fish. The pH plunges to dangerously acidic levels and marine phytoplankton dies off. Sonar testing in the oceans annihilates the ear canal of whales and the migratory patterns they have followed since the beginning of time are changing course – resulting in beached whales on shorelines all over the world.

Until we raise our awareness and accept the practice of eating fish and other sea creatures as being damaging to our health and completely unnecessary for survival we will sadly continue to disengage from our connection to the planet. We belong on land and must not interfere with aquatic life.

"The seafood industry is literally plundering the ocean of life and some fifty percent of fish caught from the oceans is fed to cows, pigs, sheep, chickens, etc in the form of fish meal. About fifty fish caught from the sea are used for each farm-raised salmon. We have turned the domestic cow into the largest marine predator on the planet. The hundreds of millions of cows grazing the land and farting methane consume more tonnage of fish than all the world's dolphins, seals and sharks combined. Domestic housecats consume more fish, especially tuna, than all the world's seals." – Captain Paul Watson, Sea Shepherd

Awakening

Today our souls are free.
No longer confined by cultural delusions, stereotypes, or political confusion.

Our minds climb like levity,
defying gravity like water flowing up ancient redwood bodies.

Our spirits have escaped the noose of modern technology, eluding expectations that buried our childhood in a labyrinth of dead ends and shattered dreams.

Today we find satisfaction in raindrops penetrating hilltops.

There is warmth emitted from clouds that block only our eyes from the sun that never stops shining.

We laugh ourselves to tears over memories of hiking through barricades that once left us feeling trapped.

We cry ourselves to awareness, leaving behind the doubts that have always sabotaged our chances of accomplishing purpose.

Today we say goodbye to uncertainty and have one last dance with shadows from graveyards of the failures of our past.

We stop planting seeds and become the soil instead, so we may nourish our beliefs with confidence and establish roots where warped thoughts once stood their ground.

We watch thick layers of ignorance drown and feel no remorse for not diving into the circus of lies that manipulate this blind society into watching wasted potential die through foreign lenses a corporate education system has plastered to our eyes.

We now paint our democracy with an untainted imagination we were gifted as a component of creation.

Today we stab temptation with the sharp blade of our inner strength and bury any misunderstandings in untapped mines that will never be exploited.

*We welcome nature as our God and kiss heaven all around us.
We find divinity in flowers and trees.*

We shower naked in waterfalls of dreams that were once abandoned by lack of opportunity.

Today our feet sink into unity with mycelium threads massaging their soles.

Our hearts begin beating in rhythm with the wind.

Now when we breathe we take in the essence of love, maintaining hope that other humans will wake up and rise above the pollutants and poisons pulling them down.

Today we stop competing for a chance to boost ego, and begin excelling at authenticating our desire to be unique individuals.

We assure our ambitions these synthetic walls and confinements will soon crash to the ground, and freedom will align with our passions.

We notice the animals trapped in zoos are staring at us, wondering why we also choose to remain locked in social taboos no different than what they are forced into.

Today we find the leader within who has been trapped beneath layers of fears.

Who has been suffocating in held back tears.

*Who was buried under plaque accumulated from years of eating what corporations manufactured from evil.
We flush our system from the lies of civilization.*

We cleanse our conscience from the mistakes we made as kids to trust the history books and doctors.

Jacoby

We break free from this American dream that was the monster hiding under our beds all along.

Today we donate our failures to the past and map out our future with fresh ideas.

We make a pact we will always do first what those who are lost put off until last.

Today we grow our angel wings of the raven and find the black jaguar within.

They carry us home to the forest, the essence of being.

Art of Nurturing

"The beautiful thing about learning is that no one can take your knowledge away from you." – B.B. King

As children, we are nurtured by our fathers, mothers, and grandmothers. This affection warms the heart. The more we receive, the sweeter we become. As we mature, we eventually separate from our familial tribe, and set off to seek knowledge and inherit wisdom around the world. Being apart from our family and loved ones, finding similar affection can be challenging. We often experience feelings of emptiness.

If you find yourself in a dark place, feeling unloved, try bringing yourself back into your sacred space. This is the space between each inhalation and exhalation. Be mindful as you breathe in fresh air from Gaia's forests. Meditate with this knowingness that you are being rewarded with fresh oxygen in each inhalation. In these moments before exhaling, remember that you are coexisting with all of life on this planet. Let your thoughts of entitlement dissipate and honor everything beautiful around you. Let nature nurture you back to your kind, loving, and harmonious way of being.

The art of nurturing teaches us that we can also feel nurtured by extending this warmth to others. When we play the role as nurturer, there is reciprocity in being affectionate for other beings. We can warm our hearts again by nurturing animals, insects, plants, and soil. We have the option to plant gardens, and nurture the soil and crops we choose to grow. We can care for house plants. We can love animals and treat all living creatures equally. We can plant trees. We can make a difference in other people's lives.

When we nurture, we find our warmth again. Confusion assembles into awareness. Hatred falls for the way generosity is always smiling. When we nurture living things and they share living energy with us, this fuels happiness. Our spirits are nourished. As we awaken, we discover the art of everything is in giving back. Even those who we do not receive from can be compensated with our grace. We keep the nurturing flow going by enriching all that is living. Kindness knows not prison.

Man Awakening – Stories of Change

While there are many disadvantages to mankind's arrogance and egoic entitlement disorders, we have potential to amass the much needed change which can shift us away from this path toward extinction to trails of abundance, cleanliness and prosperity. We need to dissolve this demand for control, drive for separation, and hunger for power.

"No one is born hating another person because of the color of his skin, or his background, or his religion. People must learn to hate, and if they can learn to hate, they can be taught to love, for love comes more naturally to the human heart."
– Nelson Mandela, *Long Walk to Freedom*

The transformation of the universal mind from a desire for profit, to a thirst for unity, requires a platform for change that permits all people from all walks of life to work toward bettering humanity rather than earning their rights to food and shelter. We never wish for anyone to lose their job or livelihood, yet the system we are entrenched in obligates some people to devote energy toward working for companies that are devastating the planet in industries that are antiquated and need to be abolished.

While government policies continue to bailout financial institutions already have enough money, and farmers who are supporting the dairy, egg and meat industries, the best solution we can manifest is using bailouts to end industries that contribute to the degradation of the planet. We all know that animal agriculture needs to end for our children, future generations and millions of species on this planet to thrive and survive. Jobs that harm Earth are impeding on our course of change and stunting our transformation. What if the World Bank and United Nations worked together to devise settlement packages for all of the multinational corporations and their employees to be reimbursed so they will be handed all of the money they need to feel satisfied in exchange for ending deleterious actions that poison us and the air, land, soil and water we depend on for survival?

Can we find a way to compensate all dairy, egg and meat farmers so they can receive payments sufficient enough to give up these methods and then shift toward more sustainable farming that only provides plant-based nourishment for mankind? This way nobody loses their job, or their livelihood, and the planet can regenerate. We can create new jobs using permaculture methods for growing and harvesting food and we can once again experience clean air and water and free up millions of acres of land for all species to thrive.

"All civilizations are impermanent and must come to an end one day. But if we continue on our current course, there is no doubt that our civilization will be destroyed sooner than we think. The Earth may need millions of years to heal, to retrieve her balance and restore her beauty. She will be able to recover, but we humans and many other species will disappear, until the Earth can generate conditions to bring us forth again in new forms. Once we can accept the impermanence of our civilization with peace, we will be liberated from our fear. Only then will we have the strength, awakening and love we need to bring us together. Cherishing our precious Earth – falling in love with the Earth – is not an obligation. This is a matter of personal and collective happiness and survival." – Thich Nhat Hanh

There are several corporations organized to promote equality, fairness and reciprocity while many more are designed to destroy in exchange for profit. If we analyze the business models set in place for companies such as Dr. Bronner's, Guayaki, Patagonia, Prana and The Body Shop we notice that the foundation of these establishments is built with the intent of giving back, preserving resources, and saving people from despair and hardship. These are companies we are encouraged to support.

"America's prosperity is an illusion that comes at great cost both to Americans and the world. This affluence is grounded in a cultural trance that alienates us from our spiritual nature and tricks our minds into using money rather than life as the measure of wealth and progress." – David Kosten

Jacoby

Rainforest Alliance is a unity of companies, consumers, farmers and forest communities committed to creating a world where nature and people thrive in harmony. The *Rainforest Alliance* (140) is an international non-profit organization working at the intersection of business, agriculture, and forests to make responsible business the new normal. *For more than thirty years this organization has been fighting deforestation and climate change. They work to build economic opportunities and better working conditions for rural people, and solve urgent environmental and social challenges.* In conjunction with their conservation partners, *they have helped prevent the deforestation of nearly 4.4 million hectares in high-risk landscapes and forest frontiers.* Rainforest Alliance has trained 1.3 million farmers around the world to build food security through sustainable agriculture. Their efforts have educated farmers to help them shift to growing methods that boost crop yields, conserve forests, protect streams and rivers, and nurture soil health. Together with these farmers, *8.6 million acres (3.5 million hectares) of agricultural land are being managed sustainably – bringing us closer to an Earth rebalanced.* The Rainforest Alliance has trained 1.3 million farmers around the world in agricultural methods that conserve forests, cultivate soil health, protect waterways, and improve livelihoods. This organization *works with indigenous and forest communities to develop innovative carbon projects that provide financial incentives for conserving or restoring forests.* Their actions demonstrate how new paradigms *interrupt the destructive cycle of poverty and deforestation – and foster a culture of conservation (rainforest-alliance.org).*

Jacque Fresco devoted his life to the *Venus Project* (141) and fought with his intellect and wit to map out a world where people can coexist with all other species without causing harm to the planet. He once said, *"When education and resources are available to all without a price tag, there will be no limit to human potential".* He believed there are no bad people, but an overload of those with insufficient information to make appropriate decisions. His goal was to *propose an alternative vision of what the future can be if what we already know in order to achieve a sustainable new civilization is applied.* The Venus Project calls for *a straightforward redesign of our culture in which the age-old inadequacies of war, poverty, hunger, debt and unnecessary human suffering are viewed not only as avoidable, but as totally unacceptable.* Anything less, he taught, *would result in a continuation of the same catalog of problems inherent in today's world.* His organization presents a feasible plan of action for social change – *one that works towards a peaceful and sustainable global civilization. Using a fresh, holistic approach dedicated to human and environmental concerns, this project outlines an alternative approach to society where human rights are no longer paper proclamations but a way of life (thevenusproject.com).*

Damian Mander is a former *Australian Royal Navy* clearance diver, and special operations military sniper. He has done twelve tours in Iraq, and was literally *programmed to destroy.* He mentions in his *TedX* speech (142) how he knows exactly how many clicks of elevation are needed to take a head-shot on a moving target from seven-hundred meters away. What is most striking about Damian's speech is how his compassion and loving nature emerged even after all he has been through. While visiting Africa, he found purpose among chaos when he saw an elephant resting on her side with a butchered face – a vicious act of poaching. At this moment he asked himself a very important question. Was he brave enough to give up his current way of living to save the lives of animals?

He decided to sell his homes, relocate to Africa, and exchange his previous life to start the *International Anti-Poaching Foundation (iapf.org).* His foundation is dedicated to protecting animals from poachers, while also guarding community assets and reducing habitat destruction. He claims that through all of his experiences, he has only performed one act of bravery that defines who he is. This was when he realized his purpose in life. He describes the decision to give up his former life to help animals by saying, *"There will never be separation between who I am, and what I do."*

The *International Anti-Poaching Foundation* was founded in 2009. They operate in Southern and East Africa, are registered in four countries and help protect over six-million acres of wilderness across the continent. *The focus of the organization is ecosystem preservation, achieved through the two key functions of training and operations. The operational model is Akashinga, a community-driven program, empowering disadvantaged women to restore and manage networks of wilderness areas. Training is conducted under the LEAD Ranger initiative, a program of excellence, building field based indigenous leadership and instructional capacity across Africa's conservation industry.*

While there are plenty of people in the world who go out of their way to help others in need, some take their compassion, generosity, and kindness and direct this passion toward saving the environment. Captain Paul Watson devotes his energy, love, and time to saving whales from whaling vessels. He and his crew risk their lives every day in efforts to save what remains of the largest, most magnificent marine mammals in the seas. Established in 1977, *Sea Shepherd Conservation Society (143)* is an international non-profit, marine wildlife conservation organization (*seashepherd.org*). Their mission is, *"To end the destruction of habitat and slaughter of wildlife in the world's oceans in order to conserve and protect ecosystems and species."* Sea Shepherd *uses innovative direct-action tactics to investigate, document, and take action when necessary to expose and confront illegal activities on the high seas. By safeguarding the biodiversity of our delicately balanced ocean ecosystems, Sea Shepherd works to ensure their survival for future generations.*

"Protecting our planet's oceans, and the marine species that call her home, is one of the most pressing sustainability crises facing humanity today and a moral imperative that we must acknowledge." – Leonardo DiCaprio

Most people recognize Leonardo DiCaprio as a talented actor. He is one of Hollywood's most well-known, and respected big names. I admire this man for his genuine love for this planet. His greatness extends far beyond the spotlight. With his earnings from those movies we enjoy so much, Mr. DiCaprio does the best he can to help save the rainforests and oceans. In addition to serving as a board member of the *World Wildlife Fund* (*worldwildlife.org*), *Oceans 5* (*oceans5.org*), *Pristine Seas*, The *Natural Resources Defense Council* (*nrdc.org*), and *International Fund for Animal Welfare* (*ifaw.org*), he also launched the *Leonardo DiCaprio Foundation* (*leonardodicaprio.com*). Mr. DiCaprio's foundation (144) is dedicated to saving the last rainforests – especially the largest remaining block of rainforest in Sumatra which is home to wild tigers, orangutans, elephants and two indigenous tribes. His team is also committed to protecting the oceans by developing strategies to stop overfishing, establish marine reserves, and save dolphins and sharks. The foundation is pledged to protect Antarctica and save melting glaciers and enthusiastic about providing access to clean water for people in Darfur, Mozambique, Sierra Leone, and Tanzania.

In 2014, Oceana (*oceana.org*), the largest international advocacy group to work on behalf of the world's oceans, received a three-million dollar grant from the *Leonardo DiCaprio Foundation* to assist with protecting threatened ocean habitat and keystone marine species such as dolphins, sharks, and whales. In November 2013, LDF awarded a three-million dollar grant to the *World Wildlife Fund* (WWF) for a bold initiative to help Nepal double its wild tiger numbers by 2022. *This grant will bolster WWF's work with the government of Nepal and local communities in Nepal's Terai Arc landscape to strengthen anti-poaching patrols, protect core areas for tiger breeding, restore critical corridors for their dispersal and expansion, and continuously monitor tiger populations. Previous support from the Leonardo DiCaprio Foundation is already showing major results, growing the number of tigers in the Terai's Bardia National Park from an estimated eighteen to fifty tigers.* Leonardo uses his fame and recognition to make the world a better place. He is a generous man who cares about animals, other people who are in need, and the environment. He shares his many gifts and extends compassion to Earth.

Philip Wollen started the *Kindness Trust* fund (*kindnesstrust.com*). He funds projects and organizations that bring kindness to our world. At the age of thirty-four, Philip became the Vice President of *Citibank*. By the age of forty, after visiting a factory farm where animals are slaughtered, he resigned and put his money and energy towards ending the factory farming industry, and enriching us with compassion. He is well known for a speech he delivered at the *St. James Ethics Debate* (145), where he argued for the removal of animal products from our menus. You can access this speech on *YouTube*. Mr. Wollen devotes his life to animals, children, the environment, the terminally ill, the homeless, and the arts. He supports over five-hundred humanitarian projects in over forty countries with schools, orphanages, shelters, sanctuaries, clinics, and scholarships. We need more leaders like him.

Julia Butterfly Hill (*juliabutterfly.com*) is an activist, author, poet, and powerful life coach who inspires her friends to live a life of passion, power, and purpose. At twenty-four, Julia was summoned to live in the canopy of an ancient redwood tree, named Luna, to help make the world aware of the plight of ancient forests. To prevent the lumber companies from cutting the tree down, she spent seven-hundred and thirty-eight days living in this beautiful tree. Her courageous act of civil disobedience gained international attention for the redwoods, as well as other environmental and social justice issues. Her efforts are chronicled in her book, *The Legacy of Luna: The Story of a Tree, a Woman, and the Struggle to Save the Redwoods*. She helps raise awareness about greed-driven logging companies and how redwood forests are critically endangered.

The *Center for Biological Diversity* (146) has one mission – saving life on Earth. This organization is comprised from the belief that *the welfare of human beings is deeply linked to nature, and to the existence in our world of a vast diversity of wild animals and plants. Because diversity has intrinsic value, and loss of biodiversity impoverishes society, this organization works to secure a future for all species with a focus on protecting the lands, waters and climate they need to survive.*

The *Center for Biological Diversity* was founded beneath the ancient ponderosa pines of New Mexico's Gila wilderness, where Kierán Suckling, Peter Galvin, and Todd Schulke met while surveying owls for the *U.S. Forest Service*. The primary driving force behind their philanthropy is *for future generations to inherit a world where the wild is still alive.* They are now fighting a growing number of national and worldwide threats to biodiversity, using legal action, and eighty-three percent of their lawsuits result in favorable outcomes.

Environment Now California promotes a transition to fully sustainable energy, food, forests and water. They aim *to preserve and restore coastal, freshwater and forest ecosystems.* The goal of their establishment is *to transform food and energy systems to create fully sustainable landscapes and urban centers.* They have teamed with the *Carbon Cycle Institute*, which is working with farmers in California to convert their farming operations to carbon farming models that can enhance ecosystem functions and provide a means for reversing climatic change.

In a 2019 *Springer Nature* journal article (147) we are informed that *half of Earth's terrestrial surface is currently in a natural condition and capable of supporting functioning ecosystems. If we are to place half of the Earth's lands under protection, we can protect all six-hundred of the sites containing the world's last homes of endangered species introduced by the Alliance for Zero Extinction Sites.* This will double at least ten key populations of the world's remaining megafauna.

While these organizations work diligently to improve the quality of air, life, soil and water globally, ask yourself how you are contributing. Are you still supporting corporations that enslave us in debt and sickness or are you taking advantage of your purchasing power to advance companies which are enhancing our well-being? Do you choose to poison your energy with political divisiveness and corruption or are you fueling your creativity and working on projects that supplement the goodness in this world? You do not need a successful organization, or team of people behind you to start making a difference individually or as a couple.

In 1998, a Brazilian couple, Lélia Deluiz Wanick Salgado and Sebastião Salgado, founded *Instituto Terra* in Brazil – an environmental organization dedicated to the sustainable development of the Valley of the River Doce. They purchased a former cattle ranch and transformed this poisoned and inarable land into a fertile woodland alive with flora and fauna – which for millenniums had made the Atlantic Forest one of the world's most important repositories of natural species. The experience shows that, with the return of vegetation, water again flows from natural springs. One result of their efforts is that Brazilian animal species at risk of extinction have again found a safe refuge.

In the last twenty years these two have collaborated with a dedicated team to plant more than two-million saplings of two-hundred and ninety-three species of trees to rejuvenate over fifteen-hundred acres of tropical forest that was devastated by cattle ranching. Their devotion to preservation and restoration have revived natural springs and controlled soil erosion. Eight of the water springs that dried up are now flowing at twenty liters per minute. The new-growth forest has generated more rainfall in the area and cooler temperatures. More than one-hundred and seventy-two species of birds, thirty-two species of mammals and fifteen species of amphibians and reptiles have migrated back to the area (148). This astounding change was accomplished by the efforts and vision of two people. Imagine if all of us dedicated energy and time toward accomplishing similar feats. We would be living in a healthier world filled with life and lush biodiversity.

I believe in the integrity and righteousness of man. I know we can eradicate this destructive and violent force which extracts the life-force of Mother Earth for material gains. Once we shatter our indoctrinated beliefs, and implant fresh perspectives, the collective consciousness of humanity will rise to a frequency that is attuned with Gaia's. We will fight with our hands and heart to protect our children, and regenerate the soil resting over new root systems. We will plant the seeds that germinate into a peaceful world, and watch as destruction is transmuted into song circles on pristine rivers beneath the shade of majestic forests lush with light and life.

Phoenix Rising

She flies to a new element – the divine – that transcends beyond confinement of imagination inside boundaries of time.

Her spirit melds with the soul of Christ – an embodiment of nature untouched by man's estrangement from wholeness.

Pure being elucidates a feeling indescribable.

Power resurrects from within that was suppressed by an inability to let knowingness emerge from her terrain.

She speaks with elevated confidence, through a compelling and mighty voice, words that are potent and clear.

The awakening of an innate and primitive consciousness.

No longer will her beliefs be limited.

She has tapped into the dissolvement of disparity.

Clarity has ripped apart the hallucinatory images fixed upon her culture, and through her fresh lens, a new Earth surfaces.

She is a seer of colors that had before gone extinct.

Bird songs flutter into her patterns of thought.

She hears the melting of struggles, evanesce of hatred, and abeyance of a carnality for conquering.

Her wings bloom as she procures her acquisition of flight through a cosmic mutiny of her senses.

She is vivacity bursting through the most fertile soil.

The growth of truce for the sustainment of equality.

A reconciliation of goodness and light.

The cessation of combat.

Amity among enmity.

Her luminosity brings concord and neutrality to fend off hostility and warfare.

She is the Phoenix Rising.

From the ashes of malice, her radiance rekindles the beauty of life.

A Paradigm Shift – Restoring Balance

The prototype for goodness is a model derived from awareness, compassion and elevated consciousness. For mankind to acquire this benevolence, we must transition to living harmoniously. Actions committed by man today are not reflective of our potentiality as a species. There is no just reason why children should be separated from their families, locked in cages, or treated as bargaining chips for political advancements. Native Americans should not be forced into reservations on small fragments of land with no clean water or healthy food available to them. They need to be granted authority over the land their ancestors were gifted to them with their creation. No longer can they be served alcohol and health-depleting foods. They deserve purity. Sacred wisdom from tribes must be restored and accepted globally. Citizens of Puerto Rico need to be respected, and their land must be released back to them. If we want to establish peace, we need to wake up from this delusion that we are free inside a paradigm where our brothers and sisters are locked in oppression. When Nelson Mandela was freed from prison after enduring twenty-seven years of incarceration for fighting to end apartheid, he said, *"I knew in that moment if I did not leave my anger and resentment behind me, my liberation would still be sealed in the penitentiary"*. He knew he had to continue his work with compassion for all people – even those who stripped him of privilege – to amass the change needed to free his people.

The unjust administration governing the United States today is an adversary to human rights. This small percentage of the population is overruling our dignity with hatred, racism and violence. Sadly, they are victims too. They are oppressed by their own confusion, ignorance and adapted hatred. They are casualties of being raised without love, unaware of what constitutes brotherhood, sisterhood, or family. They continue to feed the hungry ghost from Buddhist teachings with a lust for materialism. They are dominated by Wetiko, the parasite of the mind who thirsts for riches at the expense of inequality and injustice. The only key to their freedom is releasing control and granting liberation to those who they imprison to their greed.

There has been a cultivation of assholism through mechanisms such as alcoholism, corporate education, ecocide, egoic entitlement, nutricide, pharmaceuticals, propaganda, racial divide, societal norms and water fluoridation. To revive morality, we need to adapt a conscientious mindfulness that allows us to recognize how our actions and words impact and influence others. We need to understand that mental stamina comes from the heart, and manufactured culture depletes the heart. We need to purge the mental resiliency deficiency we have acquired. We all know something is missing and therefore must seek the insight and knowledge we hunger for. We can no longer be enslaved to illusory information, or neglect to take time to discern between what is real and what is assembled to fulfill devastating agendas. The anti-intellectualism that pervades Western civilization under the guise of universal education is our enemy.

As cells demand water for hydration, and people think they need fluids so poison the cells with alcohol, soda, wine, and fluoridated water, the mind is also craving truth. Rather than satiate this need, these same people feed the mind with lies devised by armies of goons who know no good. They widen the gap between what they feel they need and what they already have. This accentuates and elongates the voids that cripple them.

Propaganda heightens our sensitivity to man's lunacy and his denial of ecocidal activity. Corporations are burning Mother Earth and the entities responsible must be taken to trial. The judges are you and me. Our time is now to stop the wickedness that has extinction affixed to the agenda. Corrupt leaders, oligarchies, and politicians are predators. Resources and humans are their prey. We must pray every day to find ways to shut down the cycle of shame and outplay them at their own game.

The fresh new paradigm we are manifesting consists of People Embracing All Cultures Everywhere. This is the acronym and definition for PEACE. I urge you to stop feeding the monster that is poisoning us for profits. Step outside of the mainstream world, discard of your television, abstain from the alcohol, drugs, and processed foods, and get to work aiding in the restoration of nature. Stop supporting what sickens you and our planet.

Earth Mama

Earth Mama, we pray for your healing.
May your rivers flow freely.
May your trees live long.
May the birds fly peacefully.
All in alignment with your love.
With your love.

Earth Mama, may the sun always shine on you.
May your flowers always bloom.
May you keep your petroleum in your womb.
Your love for us is so true.

Earth Mama, we are warriors of your highest honor.
We fight for your protection.
We fight with our hearts, we fight with our minds, we fight with our souls.
We fight with our love.
With our love.
No weapons, no man-made destruction, no violence.
Only with love.
We are soldiers for you.

Earth mama, we pray for your healing.
No more dams, no more drilling.
No more wars, no more killing.
Only planetary healing.

Earth Mama, we know we determine your fate.
So we only touch we do not take.
Please help us save this human race, from greed and corporations.
Let us all unite as one big loving nation.
No more separation.
No more hatred or segregation.
Only unification.

Earth Mama, we are warriors of your highest honor.
We fight for your preservation.
We fight with our hearts, we fight with our minds, we fight with our souls.
We fight with our love.
With our love.
No weapons, no man-made destruction, no violence.
Only with love.
We are soldiers for you.

Earth Mama, we are your children.
We are your tribe.
We rise every morning in alignment with your love.
With your love.
Earth Mama, let us all unite as one great big nation.
Built on love.
     Built on love.

Message To Humanity

Realization is outpouring from the Central Source of creation, and I surrender to the sacred sensation of heart illumination. From this inner elevation, one can see that all paths lead to the same destination. Yes, all rivers converge at the same location – the Sea of Liberation.

With open-minded contemplation, we can find the permeation of the same core truths in every religious organization. Now the dire situation that our human race is facing is extinction or transformation, based on the collective choices humanity is making. The agenda of shadow governments is eroding the foundation of many great nations. Only a corrupt delegation needs classified documentation.

With the unsuppressed release of reverse-engineered free energy inventions, the earth shall be healed through technological innovation. We overcome all injustice through unification; and wide spread cultivation of true values, real education, and dedication to harmonious human relations.

Let the false leaders of nations feel the pains of the population. We the people have the power to stop the rise of fascist regimes and unjust corporations. Now is the time to resound our collective voice as One, and take action for all future generations.

Arise my people, you must open your eyes, before more of your freedoms are taken. Light warriors take your stations! Within yourself is salvation, the Pure Consciousness within brings the manifestation of true liberation. Illumination is bringing unification to both humans and nations.

– Jahsiah Jacobs, *Jahsiah.com*

Gaia's Grand Message

"When I planted my pain in the field of patience, a seed beneath bore fruit of happiness." – Kahlil Gibran

Mother Earth is thriving. Despite the treacherous acts of perversion and evil afflicted on her from man, she is beaming with light and life force. Even as we poison her water, pollute her air and destroy her beauty she continues to love us wholesomely. If we choose to drive our species to further endangerment, and even extinction, she will remain incorruptible and impenetrable.

The purpose of life is not to be indoctrinated with false teachings and work ourselves into debt to be enslaved to unjust regimes. Life has many purposes, and perhaps among the greatest of these is to help better the living conditions of others, and help protect our air, land, and water from poison and greed.

Merlin teaches that the crystal cave is a privileged place inside the human heart. As Earth finds security in her spirit, she cannot be harmed. When we find security from the heart, our spirit cannot be disturbed. When humans inflict harm on this Earth the damage is mirrored back to them.

The governing principles of economic prosperity circulate around chaos that diminishes entire nations and obliterates the beauty that constitutes the land. Culture has been hijacked by Walmart products and Kardashian principles. People are so delusional about what is important that they stand blindly behind the politics that poison their health, water, and the resources needed for children to live full and prosperous lives.

Regeneration of man only follows restoration of nature. With abandonment of enslavement comes freedom of mind. Water must be released from bottles and dams. Animals need liberation from all cages, labs, and zoos. As control dissolves we witness the dismantling of separation and resurrection of ethnic embrace. All skin, each tribe and every religion unites to pry open the eyes of those choosing to be sightless.

To bring balance back to Earth, the continuity of deceit and manipulation must end. Drills and mines have worn from our liking and can no longer be used for powering mankind.

In *Time of the Black Jaguar*, Arkan Lushwala introduces *munay* as *the immense power residing in the human heart that allows us to act in favor of what we love and what we want* (149). He also explains the meaning of *noka munani*. This expression of love is *holding the will and power to love and to maintain compassion in your heart*. We all experience some munay when we learn of atrocious acts that harm our planet and others. We feel a power in our heart urging us to act in defense of good. Now we must manifest the will to stand up to darkness and shatter all antiquated paradigms with purity of body, heart, mind and soul.

Carolyn Myss explains how *individual souls are active fragments of a global soul that forms the aura of all planetary life* (150). *She believes each nation has a soul that is as real as the soul occupying each human. Each nation on this planet,* from her perspective, *is an organ of one body and the health of this body rests upon each organ receiving the same care and respect. Each leader of every nation, therefore, should be understood as representatives of the collective soul of that nation.*

Thich Nhat Hanh describes the mind of man as *soil which contains several seeds that are scattered across the spectrum of dark and light.* We are encouraged to *be aware of all of them because although our ancestors may have passed on seeds of suffering to us, we were also blessed with seeds of freedom, happiness, joy and peace.* Even buried deep in our consciousness we can water them and help them grow stronger.

In *The Yellow Emperor's Internal Classic* (151), we learn of the *Source Language Grand Unification Theory*. The premise of the teaching is to understand that *the simplest truth, greatest love, purest beauty, ultimate power, deepest wisdom, and highest joy that be within everyone and everything will unite everyone and everything.* The message directs us to find a resurgence in all of our greatest attributes, share them with tribes and use the goodness you store within to regenerate land, purify water sources, release the animals, stop deforestation, and give up the drilling. As Earth again finds stability, there will be balance in the psyche of man.

Buckminster Fuller writes in *Critical Path* (152) of how *Earth is not a zero-sum Darwinian game for humans. The human mind's role is to synergize Earth into a win-win for all.* Collectively we need to awaken our consciousness and use the foundation of humanity as a means for improving quality of life. There is much more to living than alcohol, drugs, ego and television. Success does not depend on numbers reflected from our bank account. The achievements we relish in are greatest when each thread of every region is thriving. We can no longer measure success by how much materialism we acquire. Our focus must shift toward judging success based on how much we provide for others and how much our actions and work are helping to enrich the environment and landbase.

Frederick Douglass freed himself and many others from slavery by recognizing his sovereignty, and refusing to stay down. In his autobiography he wrote, *The lesson taught at this point by human experience is simply this, that the man who will get up will be helped up; and the man who will not get up will be allowed to stay down. Personal independence is a virtue and is the soul out of which comes the sturdiest manhood. There can be no independence however, without a large share of self-dependence, and this virtue cannot be bestowed. This self-appreciation must be developed from within.*

Mankind is enslaved by a power force that feeds from darkness, destruction, poison and sickness. Those who wish to be freed from this stronghold must discontinue feeding the monster. When the heavy machinery shuts off, drilling stops, chemicals are cleaned up and poison is no longer administered. The cataclysmal force diminishes and relinquishes control. Those who choose not to get up remain enslaved and contribute to the growth of this reckless power. These people depend on alcohol, drugs, pills and illusory materials to carry them through each miserable day of their life. They choose depression, sickness and struggles over working in unity to eliminate conflict. They make a conscientious choice to be part of the problems that shorten their lifespan and degrade their quality of life.

The love culture we are manifesting and cementing a foundation for is empowered by everything. We use every failure, lesson, obstacle, struggle and success to craft a world liberated from dark energies, killing, poisoning, weapons and warfare. The new world awaiting us is built with peaceful paradigms that conserve and protect animals, plants, resources and all species. Each person will be connected with all information in all languages at all times.

"When I despair, I remember that all through history the way of truth and love have always won. There have been tyrants and murderers, and for a time, they can seem invincible, but in the end, they always fall. Think of this – always." – Mahatma Gandhi

In *Braiding Sweetgrass (153)*, Robin Wall Kimmerer explains how *in the Western tradition there is a recognized hierarchy of beings, with humans being acknowledged as the pinnacle of evolution and darling of Creation.* Plants are placed at the bottom of this pyramid. She teaches how *in Native ways of knowing human people are often referred to as the younger brothers of Creation, known to possess the least experience with regard to how to live, and therefore have much to learn.* She suggests that *we must look to our teachers among other species for guidance.* She insists that *these species have been on the earth far longer than we have been, have had time to absorb the wisdom gifted from Mother Earth and that their wisdom is apparent in the way that they live.* She asserts that *if time could run backward, like a film in reverse, we would see this mess reassemble itself into lush green hills and moss-covered ledges of limestone. The streams would run back up the hills to the springs and the salt would stay glittering in underground rooms.*

"Be afraid of nothing. Hating none, giving love to all, feeling the love of God, seeing His presence in everyone, and having but one desire - for His constant presence in the temple of your consciousness - that is the way to live in this world." – Paramahansa Yogananda, In the Sanctuary of the Soul

In Marianne Williamson's book, *Imagine*, Vandana Shiva points out how *a United Nations study reveals that there is already enough food in the world, yet the problem is one of distribution.* She shares how *the world is producing the wrong kind of food using processes that leave millions of people cashless, homeless, landless and unable to feed themselves.* She preaches how *rich sources of nutrition disappear with the destruction of diversity, and pierces our precepts by letting us know that monoculture of the mind creates monoculture in the fields* (154).

Lance Secretan explains that *half of the world's largest economies are corporations – not nations. No other institutions – not the great religions or the world's political systems – have as much reach, intellect, power, talent, money, or therefore opportunity to influence the world. Learning is an inoculation against irrelevance* (155). For harmony on Earth to rekindle we must use communication and technology to bring information to all people in an open-source system where nothing is kept secret and no tribe in any region of the world is left in the dark.

To live on this land we inherited from native ancestors, we are entitled to honoring and respecting the beauty of Earth in a manner similar to Chief Seattle. His spirit still fights for us to adapt the change needed to bring back the purity which he and his people were acquainted with. We must lead by example. Be the person you always needed as a child. Befriend Mother Earth and aid her transformation. Be a force of light this planet needs for regeneration and restoration. Let love be your mantra.

"There is a revolution that needs to happen which starts from inside each of us. We need to wake up and fall in love with Earth. We have been homo sapiens for a long time. Now is the time to become homo-conscious. Our love and admiration for Earth has the power to unite us and remove all boundaries, separation and discrimination. Centuries of individualism and competition have brought about tremendous destruction and alienation. We need to re-establish true communication–true communion–with ourselves, with Earth, and with one another as children of the same mother." – Thich Nhat Hanh

Your Love

> *"Everyone is a moon, and has a dark side, which he never shows anyone."* – Mark Twain

I was alive before the heartbeat. This life force activated my embryonic development. An energy unmatched. Garnering celestial consciousness.

I was already here, before I listened with ears. I sensed the aroma of redwood soil prior to having a nose. I touched nature all over her body and felt true sensation dating back to a time when I had no fingers or nerves. I saw the perfection of forests and oceans. I admired colors that have since gone extinct. I have always been immersed in the never ending beauty of this Earth.

I loved you back when trees still stood high. The brightness of Grandfather moon lit up the sky. We could see mountains for miles. Glaciers were as big as your smile.

You enchanted my soul before grass beneath pavement, when there was no deforestation, and mines still stored precious metals locked in time.

I admired how untamed and wild your spirits flame was flying. I was watching – before haze and pollution – when stars were reflections of your love. Nothing got me higher.

Before bombs, factory farms, and guns there was a world with a sweet and friendly sun shining out on everyone.

Your love. The disarmament of guns. The patterns of the phalangeals on your fingers. Your grace fills me with purity.

I watch you fly, with wings like eagles, planting seeds to a world freed from greed.

> *"The gem cannot be polished without friction, nor man perfected without trials."* – Confucius

Author's Epilogue

"The soul would have no rainbow if the eye had no tears."
– Native American wisdom

Education fascinates me. The vast knowledge that is disseminated to us when we abolish discrimination and suppression surpasses all elementary information we are indoctrinated with in the universal education system. I have been showered with the love and wisdom from Gaia, spirit of this beautiful Mother Earth. I was reacquainted with wisdom from the first Choctaw chief, Moshulatubbee, and the great Choctaw warrior, Pushmataha. I felt the sharp sword of Archangel Michael piercing me with clarity. I sipped from the cup of death only to find myself drinking again from the light of life. For the blessings in my life I will always be forever grateful, and feel eternally indebted to the spirits who guide me on this life path.

As these lessons were woven through layers of my soul, I embraced the brightest light I have ever witnessed emanating from the spirit of Mother Earth. She helped me integrate her lessons of purity and truth into the pages of this book. My heart opened. I felt a connection with nature unlike ever before. This project awakened my consciousness, and inspired me to be a source of radiance everywhere I go.

When we stop buying what keeps us oppressed, we begin to purchase our liberation. My greatest acquisition I inherited from writing this book was learning to always stand for what I know in my heart is pure. I hope you will also use these lessons to adapt a healthier lifestyle and care more for this Earth that nourishes us with abundance, and nurtures us with seeds of compassion, grace, hope, love, and truth. May we coexist with all beings who we share this land with. May the goodness of mankind blossom from the darkness that has cast shadows over our potential. Together we will spring forth the change needed to preserve the beauty on this planet for the next seven generations.

"Crying peace is no longer enough. We must act peace, live peace, and live in peace." – Shenandoah

About the Author

Jesse Jacoby is a dedicated father and advocate for compassion, equanimity, human rights, indigenous freedom, veganism and world peace. He devotes his time and expends energy toward gathering teachings and devising strategies for establishing new paradigms that make preexisting patterns and ideologies which are not reflective of goodness obsolete.

Jesse is part Choctaw native and a promoter of equality for all. He serves as a plant-based nutrition consultant and is CEO of Soulspire (*soulspire.com*), an educational program orchestrated to teach people how to adapt to living a healthy lifestyle congruent with the betterment of this planet we all depend on for survival.

Jesse's teachings are simple. He encourages his readers and students to be mindful of their purchasing power and to contribute as much as possible to supporting endeavors that commit to improving the quality of air, life, soil and water on Earth. He is the author of The Raw Cure: Healing Beyond Medicine, Society's Anonymous, My Quest To Conquer What Matters, and Eating Plant-Based: The New Health Paradigm. He also enjoys spoken word poetry and has an album titled Soulfire.

Jesse@soulspire.com

Bibliography

1.) Dubos René J. *Man Adapting*. Yale University Press, 1980.

2.) Tompkins, P., & Bird, C. (2007). *The secret life of plants*. Princeton, N.J: Recording for the Blind & Dyslexic.

3.) Coffey, Don, De Marzo, Angelo. Evolution and Prostate Cancer. Prostate Cancer Update. Winter 2000

4.) Roberts, William. The Cause of Atherosclerosis. Nutrition In Clinical Practice. Vol 23, Issue 5, 2008

5.) Robinson, Simon D. Meatonomics. Berkeley, CA: CONARI PRESS,U.S, 2013. Print.

6.) Varki, A. Uniquely Human Evolution of Sialic Acid Genetics and Biology. National Academy of Sciences. May 11, 2010 vol. 107

7.) Samraj, A.N, O.M.T Pearce, H Laubli, A.N Crittenden, A.K Bergfeld, K Band, C.J Gregg, A.E Bingman, P Secrest, S.L Diaz, N.M Varki, A Varki, N.M Varki, A Varki, and S.A Kornfeld. "A Red Meat-Derived Glycan Promotes Inflammation and Cancer Progression." Proceedings of the National Academy of Sciences of the United States of America. 112.2 (2015): 542-547

8.) Ji, S, F Wang, Y Chen, C Yang, P Zhang, X Zhang, F A. Troy, and B Wang. "Developmental Changes in the Level of Free and Conjugated Sialic Acids, Neu5ac, Neu5gc and Kdn in Different Organs of Pig: a Lc-Ms/ms Quantitative Analyses." Glycoconjugate Journal. 34.1 (2017): 21-30

9.) WARREN, L, and H FELSENFELD. "The Biosynthesis of Sialic Acids." The Journal of Biological Chemistry. 237 (1962): 1421-31

10.) Varki, A, and P Gagneux. "Multifarious Roles of Sialic Acids in Immunity." Annals of the New York Academy of Sciences. 1253 (2012): 16-36

11.) Taylor, Rachel E, Christopher J. Gregg, Vered Padler-Karavani, Darius Ghaderi, Hai Yu, Shengshu Huang, Ricardo U. Sorensen, Xi Chen, Jaime Inostroza, Victor Nizet, and Ajit Varki. "Novel Mechanism for the Generation of Human Xeno-Autoantibodies against the Nonhuman Sialic Acid N-Glycolylneuraminic Acid." The Journal of Experimental Medicine. 207.8 (2010): 1637

12.) Fields, H. Is Meat Killing Us? The Journal of the American Osteopathic Association, May 2016, 296-300

13.) Steinberg, Helmut O, Basel Bayazeed, Ginger Hook, Ann Johnson, Jessica Cronin, and Alain D. Baron. "Endothelial Dysfunction Is Associated with Cholesterol Levels in the High Normal Range in Humans." *Circulation*. 96.10 (1997): 3287

14.) Campbell, T C, and Thomas M. Campbell. *The China Study: The Most Comprehensive Study of Nutrition Ever Conducted and the Startling Implications for Diet, Weight Loss and Long-Term Health.* , 2016. Print.

15.) Koeth, RA, Z Wang, BS Levison, JA Buffa, E Org, BT Sheehy, EB Britt, X Fu, Y Wu, L Li, JD Smith, JA DiDonato, J Chen, H Li, GD Wu, JD Lewis, M Warrier, JM Brown, RM Krauss, WH Tang, FD Bushman, AJ Lusis, and SL Hazen. "Intestinal Microbiota Metabolism of L-Carnitine, a Nutrient in Red Meat, Promotes Atherosclerosis." *Nature Medicine*. 19.5 (2013): 576-85

16.) Koeth, RA, BS Levison, MK Culley, JA Buffa, Z Wang, JC Gregory, E Org, Y Wu, L Li, JD Smith, WH Tang, JA DiDonato, AJ Lusis, and SL Hazen. "Γ-butyrobetaine Is a Proatherogenic Intermediate in Gut Microbial Metabolism of L-Carnitine to Tmao." *Cell Metabolism*. 20.5 (2014): 799-812

17.) Tang, W H. W, Z Wang, D J. Kennedy, Y Wu, J A. Buffa, B Agatisa-Boyle, X S. Li, B S. Levison, and S L. Hazen. "Gut Microbiota-Dependent Trimethylamine N-Oxide (tmao) Pathway Contributes to Both Development of Renal Insufficiency and Mortality Risk in Chronic Kidney Disease." *Circulation Research*. 116.3 (2015): 448-455

18.) Zhu, Weifei, Jill C. Gregory, Elin Org, Jennifer A. Buffa, Nilaksh Gupta, Zeneng Wang, Lin Li, Xiaoming Fu, Yuping Wu, Margarete Mehrabian, R B. Sartor, Thomas M. McIntyre, Roy L. Silverstein, W.H W. Tang, Joseph A. DiDonato, J M. Brown, Aldons J. Lusis, and Stanley L. Hazen. "Gut Microbial Metabolite Tmao Enhances Platelet Hyperreactivity and Thrombosis Risk." *Cell*. 165.1 (2016): 111-124.

19.) Senthong, V, Z Wang, Y Fan, Y Wu, SL Hazen, and WH Tang. "Trimethylamine N-Oxide and Mortality Risk in Patients with Peripheral Artery Disease." *Journal of the American Heart Association*. 5.10 (2016)

20.) FACLM, Michael Greger M.D. "PhIP: The Three-Strikes Breast Carcinogen." *NutritionFacts.org*, Jan. 2013, nutritionfacts.org/video/phip-the-three-strikes-breast-carcinogen/.

21.) Rohrmann, S, J Linseisen, Jung S.-U. Lukas, and W Pfau. "Dietary Intake of Meat and Meat-Derived Heterocyclic Aromatic Amines and Their Correlation with Dna Adducts in Female Breast Tissue." *Mutagenesis*. 24.2 (2009): 127-132

22.) Holland, Ricky D, Theresa Gehring, Jason Taylor, Brian G. Lake, Nigel J. Gooderham, and Robert J. Turesky. "Formation of a Mutagenic Heterocyclic Aromatic Amine from Creatinine in Urine of Meat Eaters and Vegetarians." *Chemical Research in Toxicology*. 18.3 (2005): 579-590.

23.) Boyland, Eric, and Alfred A. Levi. "Metabolism of Polycyclic Compounds." *Biochemical Journal*. 30.4 (1936): 728-731.

24.) Bouvard, Véronique, Dana Loomis, Kathryn Z. Guyton, Yann Grosse, Fatiha E. Ghissassi, Lamia Benbrahim-Tallaa, Neela Guha, Heidi Mattock, and Kurt Straif. "Carcinogenicity of Consumption of Red and Processed Meat." *The Lancet Oncology*. 16.16 (2015): 1599-1600

25.) Ornish, Dean, Jue Lin, June M. Chan, Elissa Epel, Colleen Kemp, Gerdi Weidner, Ruth Marlin, Steven J. Frenda, Mark J. M. Magbanua, Jennifer Daubenmier, Ivette Estay, Nancy K. Hills, Nita Chainani-Wu, Peter R. Carroll, and Elizabeth H. Blackburn. "Effect of Comprehensive Lifestyle Changes on Telomerase Activity and Telomere Length in Men with Biopsy-Proven Low-Risk Prostate Cancer: 5-Year Follow-Up of a Descriptive Pilot Study." *The Lancet Oncology*. 14.11 (2013): 1112-1120

26.) Restriction of Meat, Fish, and Poultry in Omnivores Improves Mood: a Pilot Randomized Controlled Trial. BioMed Central, 2012

27.) David, LA, CF Maurice, RN Carmody, DB Gootenberg, JE Button, BE Wolfe, AV Ling, AS Devlin, Y Varma, MA Fischbach, SB Biddinger, RJ Dutton, and PJ Turnbaugh. "Diet Rapidly and Reproducibly Alters the Human Gut Microbiome." *Nature*. 505.7484 (2014): 559-63.

28.) Liebig, Justus Von. *Familiar Letters on Chemistry*. Rarebooksclub Com, 2012.

29.)Lösch, Sandra, Negahnaz Moghaddam, Karl Grossschmidt, Daniele U. Risser, Fabian Kanz, and Clark S. Larsen. "Stable Isotope and Trace Element Studies on Gladiators and Contemporary Romans from Ephesus (turkey, 2nd and 3rd Ct. Ad) - Implications for Differences in Diet." *Plos One*. 9.10 (2014)

30.)*Institute of Medicine, Dietary Reference Intakes for Energy, Carbohydrate, Fiber, Fat, Fatty Acids, Cholesterol, Protein, and Amino Acids (Macronutrients)*. 2005, National Academies Press: Washington, DC.

31.) Dina, Karin, and Rick Dina. *The Raw Food Nutrition Handbook: An Essential Guide to Understanding Raw Food Diets*. , 2015.

32.) Kulvinskas, Viktoras P. *Survival into the 21st Century: Planetary Healers Manual*. Woodstock Valley, Ct: 21st Century Publications, 1999. Print.

33.) Jacoby, Jesse. *Eating Plant-Based: The New Health Paradigm*. Soulspire Publishing, 2017.

34.) May2019,cen.acs.org/acs-news/programs/CAS-reaches-150-millionth-substance/97/web/2019/05.

35.) Neltner, T G, H M. Alger, J E. Leonard, and M V. Maffini. "Data Gaps in Toxicity Testing of Chemicals Allowed in Food in the United States." *Reproductive Toxicology New York*. 42 (2013): 85-94.

36.) Oates, Liza, Marc Cohen, Lesley Braun, Adrian Schembri, and Rilka Taskova. "Reduction in Urinary Organophosphate Pesticide Metabolites in Adults After a Week-Long Organic Diet." *Environmental Research*. 132 (2014): 105-111.

37.) Faber,Scott."1,000Chemicals."*EWG*,May2014,www.ewg.org/enviroblog/2014/05/1000-chemicals.

38.)"Zeitgeist: The Movie--The Greatest Story Ever Told." Sideways Film, 2008.

39.) Levy, Paul. *Dispelling Wetiko: Breaking the Curse of Evil* . North Atlantic Books, 2013.

40.)*Consumer Reports Survey: One In Four People Who Regularly Take Meds Hit with Sticker Shock at the Pharmacy*, www.consumerreports.org/media-room/press releases/2017/05/consumer_reports_survey_one_in_four_people_who_regularly_take_meds_hit_with_sticker_shock_at_the_pharmacy/.

41.) Office, U.S. Government Accountability. "Drug Industry: Profits, Research and Development Spending, and Merger and Acquisition Deals." *U.S. Government Accountability Office (U.S. GAO)*, 19 Dec. 2017, www.gao.gov/products/GAO-18-40.

42.) Rowlatt, Justin. "How the US Military's Opium War in Afghanistan Was Lost." *BBC News*, BBC, 25 Apr. 2019, www.bbc.com/news/world-us-canada-47861444.

43.) Matar, Sami, and Lewis F. Hatch. *Chemistry of Petrochemical Processes:* Gulf Publ., 2005

44.)"American Cancer Society." *Wikipedia*, Wikimedia Foundation, 1 July 2019, en.wikipedia.org/wiki/American_Cancer_Society.

45.)"Cancer." *World Health Organization*, World Health Organization, www.who.int/news-room/fact-sheets/detail/cancer.

46.) "2018 NCI Budget Fact Book - Research Funding." *National Cancer Institute*, 2018, www.cancer.gov/about-nci/budget/fact-book/data/research-funding.

47.) Mawson AR, Ray BD, Bhuiyan AR, Jacob B (2017) Pilot comparative study on the health of vaccinated and unvaccinated 6- to 12-year-old U.S. children. J Transl Sci 3: DOI: 10.15761/JTS.1000186

48.) Smith, Timothy. The GcMAF Book. 2010

49.) Yamamoto N, Urade M, Ueda M. 2005. Potent tumoricidal capacity of macrophages activated by Gc protein-derived macrophage activating factor (GcMAF) and its therapeutic efficacy for prostate, breast, and colorectal cancers. J Immunother 28:642.

50.) Ambrose M, Gostic KM, Et al. Potent protection against H5N1 and H7N9 influenza via childhood hemagglutinin imprinting. Science. 2016 Nov 11;354(6313):722-726.

51.) Zerbo, Ousseny et al. "Association Between Influenza Infection and Vaccination During Pregnancy and Risk of Autism Spectrum Disorder." JAMA pediatrics 171 1 (2017): e163609 .

52.) Mold, Matthew et al. "Aluminium in brain tissue in autism." Journal of trace elements in medicine and biology : organ of the Society for Minerals and Trace Elements 46 (2018): 76-82 .

53.) *Tomljenovic, Lucija and Christopher A. Shaw. "Aluminum vaccine adjuvants: are they safe?" Current medicinal chemistry 18 17 (2011): 2630-7 .*

54.) *Miller, Neil Z.. "Aluminum in Childhood Vaccines Is Unsafe." (2016).*

55.) *Vargas, Diana L. Torres et al. "Neuroglial activation and neuroinflammation in the brain of patients with autism." Annals of neurology 57 1 (2005): 67-81 .*

56.) *Shaw, Christopher A. and Michael Steven Petrik. "Aluminum hydroxide injections lead to motor deficits and motor neuron degeneration." Journal of inorganic biochemistry 103 11 (2009): 1555-62* .

57.) Patterson, Paul H. (2006) *Pregnancy, Immunity, Schizophrenia, and Autism.* Engineering and Science, 69 (3). pp. 10-21. ISSN 0013-7812

58.)*Christian, Lisa M et al. "Inflammatory responses to trivalent influenza virus vaccine among pregnant women." Vaccine 29 48 (2011): 8982-7* .

59.)*Zerbo, Ousseny et al. "Association Between Influenza Infection and Vaccination During Pregnancy and Risk of Autism Spectrum Disorder." JAMA pediatrics 171 1 (2017): e163609* .

60.) "Childhood Cancer Statistics: CureSearch." *CureSearch for Children's Cancer*, curesearch.org/Childhood-Cancer-Statistics.

61.) "Number of Children & Adolescents Taking Psychiatric Drugs in the U.S." *CCHR International*, 27 Sept. 2018, www.cchrint.org/psychiatric-drugs/children-on-psychiatric-drugs/.

62.) "Autism Facts and Figures." *Autism Speaks*, www.autismspeaks.org/autism-facts-and-figures.

63.)"National Statistics on Child Abuse." *National Childrens Alliance*, www.nationalchildrensalliance.org/media-room/nca-digital-media-kit/national-statistics-on-child-abuse/.

64.)*Bercik, Premysl et al. "The intestinal microbiota affect central levels of brain-derived neurotropic factor and behavior in mice." Gastroenterology 141 2 (2011): 599-609, 609.e1-3* .

65.) Mulinari, Shai. "Monoamine theories of depression: historical impact on biomedical research". *Journal of the History of the Neurosciences.* 2012, 21(4). 366-392.

66.) *Meyer, Jeffrey H. et al. "Elevated monoamine oxidase a levels in the brain: an explanation for the monoamine imbalance of major depression." Archives of general psychiatry 63 11 (2006): 1209-16* .

67.) *Clarke, Sarah E. Dixon and Rona R. Ramsay. "Dietary inhibitors of monoamine oxidase A." Journal of Neural Transmission 118 (2010): 1031-1041.*

68.)*Palhano-Fontes, Fernanda et al. "Rapid antidepressant effects of the psychedelic ayahuasca in treatment-resistant depression: a randomized placebo-controlled trial." Psychological medicine (2019).*

69.) Uthaug, M.V., van Oorsouw, K., Kuypers, K.P.C. et al. Psychopharmacology (2018) 235: 2979. https://doi.org/10.1007/s00213-018-4988-3

70.) Tsai AC, Chang TL, Chi SH. Frequent consumption of vegetables predicts lower risk of depression in older Taiwanese - results of a prospective population-based study. Public Health Nutr 2012;15:1087–92.

71.)*Beezhold, Bonnie Lynn and Carol S Johnston. "Restriction of meat, fish, and poultry in omnivores improves mood: A pilot randomized controlled trial." Nutrition journal (2012).*

72.)*Gomez-Pinilla, Fernando and Trang Thu Nguyen. "Natural mood foods: the actions of polyphenols against psychiatric and cognitive disorders." Nutritional neuroscience 15 3 (2012): 127-33* .

73.) Rossi, L., Mazzitelli, S., Arciello, M. et al. Neurochem Res (2008) 33: 2390.

74.) Kanti Bhooshan Pandey and Syed Ibrahim Rizvi, "Plant Polyphenols as Dietary Antioxidants in Human Health and Disease," Oxidative Medicine and Cellular Longevity, vol. 2, no. 5, pp. 270-278, 2009.

75.)*Beezhold, Bonnie Lynn et al. "Vegetarian diets are associated with healthy mood states: a cross-sectional study in Seventh Day Adventist adults." Nutrition journal (2010).*

76.) Harker, Alexandra. "Landscapes of the Dead: an Argument for Conservation Burial." (2012).

77.) Sample, Ian. "Polar Express: Magnetic North Pole Speeds towards Russia." *The Guardian*, Guardian News and Media, 5 Feb. 2019, www.theguardian.com/world/2019/feb/05/magnetic-north-pole-moving-pretty-fast-towards-russia.

78.) Liou, J.-C, and et al. "NASA ODPO's Large Constellation Study ." *NASA Orbitaal Debris Quarterly News*, 2018, orbitaldebris.jsc.nasa.gov/quarterly-news/pdfs/odqnv22i3.pdf.

79.) Williamson, Marianne. *Imagine: What America Could Be in the 21st Century: Visions of a Better Future from Leading American Thinkers*. New American Library, 2001.

80.) Initiative, Rights and Resources. "Who Owns the Land in Africa?" *Rights + Resources*, Oct. 2015, rightsandresources.org/en/publication/who-owns-the-land-in-africa/#.XUa-KEcnbIU.

81.) Rieffel, Lex, and James Fox. "The Millennium Challenge Corporation." *Brookings Global Economy and Development*, 2008, www.brookings.edu/wp-content/uploads/2016/06/12_mcc_rieffel.pdf.

82.)*Gray, Mark Allan* (1996) "The International Crime of *Ecocide*," *California Western International Law* Journal: Vol. 26 : No. 2 , Article 3.

83.)"End Ecocide in Europe: A Citizens' Initiative to Give the Earth Rights ." *Initiative Details - European Citizens' Initiative - European Commission*, 4 Jan. 2012, ec.europa.eu/citizens-initiative/public/initiatives/obsolete/details/2012/000012.

84.) Higgins, P., Short, D. & South, N. Crime Law Soc Change (2013) 59: 251.

85.) Yinon M. Bar-On, Rob Phillips, and Ron Milo. *The biomass distribution on Earth*. PNAS June 19, 2018 115 (25) 6506-651

86.)IPBES. 2019. Summary for policymakers of the global assessment report on biodiversity and ecosystem services of the Intergovernmental Science-Policy Platform on Biodiversity and Ecosystem Services

87.) Smith, Zak. "Natural Ecosystem Collapse Demands Transformative Change." *NRDC*, 30 Apr. 2019, www.nrdc.org/experts/zak-smith/transformative-change-will-stop-natural-ecosystem-collapse.

88.) Schiermeier, Quirin. "Eat less meat: UN climate change report calls for change to human diet." Nature International Journal of Science. Aug. 2019. <https://www.nature.com/articles/d41586-019-02409-7>.

89.)USI. "Paper Recycling Facts." *University of Southern Indiana*, www.usi.edu/recycle/paper-recycling-facts/.

90.) Skene, Jennifer, and Shelley Vinyard. "The Issue with Tissue: How Americans Are Flushing Forests Down the Toilet." *NRDC*, 28 Feb. 2019, www.nrdc.org/resources/issue-tissue-how-americans-are-flushing-forests-down-toilet.

91-94.) Jensen, Derrick, and George Draffan. *Strangely like War: the Global Assault on Forests*. Green Books, 2004.

95.) Ground Water Protection Council. "Modern Shale Gas Development in the United States: A Primer." *Energy.gov*, 2013, www.energy.gov/fe/downloads/modern-shale-gas-development-united-states-primer.

96.) Pinchetti, Sophie. "Waorani People Win Landmark Legal Victory Against Ecuadorian Government." *Amazon Frontlines*, 30 Apr. 2019, www.amazonfrontlines.org/chronicles/waorani-victory/.

97.)*McGlade, Christophe and Paul Ekins. "The geographical distribution of fossil fuels unused when limiting global warming to 2 °C." Nature 517 (2015): 187-190.*

98.)"Landmark U.S. Federal Climate Lawsuit." *Our Children's Trust*, 2019, www.ourchildrenstrust.org/juliana-v-us.

99.) Steele, Robert David. *Intelligence for Earth: Clarity, Integrity, & Sustainability*. Earth Intelligence Network, 2010.

100.)"Ocean Plastics Pollution - A Global Tragedy for Our Oceans and Sea Life." *Ocean Plastics Pollution*, 2019, www.biologicaldiversity.org/campaigns/ocean_plastics/.

101.) The Ocean Cleanup. "The Great Pacific Garbage Patch." *The Ocean Cleanup*, 2019, theoceancleanup.com/great-pacific-garbage-patch/.

102.) Ryan P.G. (2015) A Brief History of Marine Litter Research. In: Bergmann M., Gutow L., Klages M. (eds) Marine Anthropogenic Litter. Springer, Cham

103.) Northern Rocky Mountain Science Center. "Retreat of Glaciers in Glacier National Park." *Retreat of Glaciers in Glacier National Park*, USGS, 2016, www.usgs.gov/centers/norock/science/retreat-glaciers-glacier-national-park?qt-science_center_objects=0#qt-science_center_objects.

104.) Mimura, Nobuo. Sea-level rise caused by climate change and its implications for society. Proc Jpn Acad Ser B Phys Biol Sci. 2013 Jul 25; 89(7): 281–301.

105.) Leahy, Stephen. "Greenland's Ice Is Melting Four Times Faster than Thought-What It Means." *National Geographic*, 21 Jan. 2019, www.nationalgeographic.com/environment/2019/01/greeland-ice-melting-four-times-

106.) Vijay, Varsha et al. *"The Impacts of Oil Palm on Recent Deforestation and Biodiversity Loss." PloS one (2016)*.

107.)"2.6 Billion Pounds of Monsanto's Glyphosate Sprayed on U.S. Farmland in Past Two Decades." *EcoWatch*, EcoWatch, 31 Jan. 2019, www.ecowatch.com/2-6-billion-pounds-of-monsantos-glyphosate-sprayed-on-u-s-farmland-in--1882107186.html.

108.) Benbrook, Charles M.. *"Trends in glyphosate herbicide use in the United States and globally." Environmental Sciences Europe (2016)*.

109.) Zhang, L, Rana, I, et al. Exposure to glyphosate-based herbicides and risk for non-Hodgkin lymphoma: A meta-analysis and supporting evidence. Mutat Res. 2019 Feb 10;781:186-206. doi: 10.1016/j.mrrev.2019.02.001.

110.)Sánchez-Bayo, Francisco and K A G Wyckhuys. *"Worldwide decline of the entomofauna: A review of its drivers." (2019)*.

111.) Arsenault, Chris. "Only 60 Years of Farming Left If Soil Degradation Continues." *Scientific American*, www.scientificamerican.com/article/only-60-years-of-farming-left-if-soil-degradation-continues/.

112.) Gomiero, Tiziano. *"Soil Degradation, Land Scarcity and Food Security: Reviewing a Complex Challenge." (2016)*.

113.)"SCoPEx." *SCoPEx*, 2019, projects.iq.harvard.edu/keutschgroup/scopex.

114.) Isaksen, Ivar S. A. et al. "Atmospheric composition change: climate-chemistry interactions." (2009).

115.) Atkinson, Joe. "Smoke from Wildfires Can Have Lasting Climate Impact." *NASA*, NASA, 12 June 2017, www.nasa.gov/feature/langley/smoke-from-wildfires-can-have-lasting-climate-impact/.

116.) Ludmil B. Alexandrov, Young Seok Ju, et al. Mutational signatures associated with tobacco smoking in human cancer. *Science*04 Nov 2016 : 618-622

117.)"How You Can Conserve Water." *Water Conservation Facts and Tips | National Geographic*, 18 June 2019, www.nationalgeographic.com/environment/freshwater/water-conservation-tips/?source=link_two8172010n.

118.)"What Is the Water-Energy-Food Nexus." *Water Footprint Calculator*, 3 Dec. 2018, www.watercalculator.org/footprints/water-energy-food-nexus/.

119.) University of California Agriculture and Natural Resources. "Cultivating Solutions in Ventura County." *University of California Cooperative Extension Ventura*, ceventura.ucanr.edu/index4.cfm?blogpost=16023&blogasset=19305.

120.) Sodium Fluoride. Material Safety Data Sheet. Sigma Chemical Co., www.fluoridealert.org/wp-content/pesticides/sodium.fluoride.msds.1999.htm.

121.) Barbier, Olivier C et al. *"Molecular mechanisms of fluoride toxicity."* Chemico-biological interactions 188 2 (2010): 319-33 .

122.) Oberheu, Caroline. "Where Are Grapes Grown?" *WorldAtlas*, 23 Aug. 2016, www.worldatlas.com/articles/top-grape-growing-countries.html.

123.) "Roundup's Toxic Chemical Glyphosate, Found In 100% Of California Wines Tested." *Wine and Water Watch*, winewaterwatch.org/2018/02/roundups-toxic-chemical-glyphosate-found-in-100-of-california-wines-tested/.

124.) Kalinin, Sergey I. et al. "Transcriptome analysis of alcohol-treated microglia reveals downregulation of beta amyloid phagocytosis." Journal of Neuroinflammation (2018).

125.) Burton, Robyn, Hydes, Theresa, et al. A comparison of gender-linked population cancer risks between alcohol and tobacco. *BMC Public Health* volume 19, Article number: 316 (2019)

126.) "Farm Life Frequently Asked Questions." *Midwest Dairy*, www.midwestdairy.com/education/farm-life/farm-life-faq/.

127.) "Pollution." *Down to Earth Organic and Natural*, www.downtoearth.org/categories/environment/pollution.

128.) Poore, J and T Nemecek. "Reducing food's environmental impacts through producers and consumers." Science 360 (2018): 987-992.

129.) Steinfeld, Henning. *Livestock's Long Shadow*: Environmental Issues and Options. Rome: Food and Agriculture Organization of the United Nations, 2006. Print.

130.) "U.S. Farming: Total Number of Farms 2018." *Statista*, www.statista.com/statistics/196103/number-of-farms-in-the-us-since-2000/.

131.) "Basic Information about Nonpoint Source (NPS) Pollution." *EPA*, Environmental Protection Agency, 10 Aug. 2018, www.epa.gov/nps/basic-information-about-nonpoint-source-nps-pollution.

132.) "Nonpoint Source: Agriculture." *EPA*, Environmental Protection Agency, 18 Aug. 2017, www.epa.gov/nps/nonpoint-source-agriculture.

133.) Hribar, Carrie. *Understanding Concentrated Animal Feeding Operations and Their Impact on Communities*. National Association of Local Boards of Health, 2010, www.cdc.gov/nceh/ehs/docs/understanding_cafos_nalboh.pdf.

134.) Glass Web Projects, LLC. "Factory Farm Waste Solutions." *Hoosier Environmental Council*, www.hecweb.org/issues/environmental-health-justice/factory-farm-waste/.

135.) "Pollution (Water, Air, Chemicals)." *Food Empowerment Project*, foodispower.org/environmental-and-global/pollution-water-air-chemicals/.

136.) Brooks, Myron, Smith, Richard L., et al. In Situ Stimulation of Groundwater Denitrification with Formate To Remediate Nitrate Contamination. *Environ. Sci. Technol.* 2001351196-203

137.) Kaye H. Kilburn, "Human Impairment from Living near Confined Animal (Hog) Feeding Operations," Journal of Environmental and Public Health, vol. 2012, Article ID 565690, 11 pages, 2012. https://doi.org/10.1155/2012/565690.

138.) "The USDA's War on Wildlife." *Predator Defense - The USDA Wildlife Services' War on Wildlife*, www.predatordefense.org/USDA.htm.

139.) "Environmental Security." *Stimson Center*, 13 June 2017, www.stimson.org/programs/environmental-security.

140.)"Home." *Rainforest Alliance*, www.rainforest-alliance.org/about.

141.)"About." *The Venus Project*, www.thevenusproject.com/the-venus-project/.

142.)"Damien Mander - Modern Warrior Ted Talk - IAPF." *International Anti-Poaching Foundation*, 14 Apr. 2017, www.iapf.org/modern-warrior-damien-mander-tedxsydney/.

143.)"Our History." *Sea Shepherd*, 6 Mar. 2018, seashepherd.org/our-history/.

144.)"About   Us."   *The   Leonardo   DiCaprio   Foundation*, www.leonardodicaprio.org/about/.

145.)"Philip Wollen, Australian Philanthropist, Former VP of Citibank, Animals Should Be   Off   the   Menu   Debate."   *Humane   Decisions*,   20   Apr.   2019, www.humanedecisions.com/philip-wollen-australian-philanthropist-former-vp-of-citibank-animals-should-be-off-the-menu-debate/.

146.)*Our Story*, www.biologicaldiversity.org/about/story/.

147.)"Achieving   the   Paris   Climate   Agreement   Goals."   *Www.springer.com*, www.springer.com/gp/about-springer/media/press-releases/corporate/achieving-the-paris-climate-agreement-goals/16443362.

148.)*INSTITUTO   TERRA   -   WELCOME   -   Official   Website* www.institutoterra.org/eng/conteudosLinks.php?id=22&tl=QWJvdXQgdXM&sb=NQ.

149.) Lushwala, Arkan. *The Time of the Black Jaguar:* Createspace, 2013.

150.) Williamson, Marianne. *Imagine: What America Could Be in the 21st Century: Visions of a Better Future from Leading American Thinkers*. New American Library, 2001.

151.) Veith, Ilza. *Huang Ti Nei Ching Su wên = The Yellow Emperor's Classic of Internal Medicine*. University of California Press, 2016.

152.) Fuller, Richard Buckminster. *Critical Path*. St. Martin's Press, 1981.

153.) Kimmerer, Robin Wall. *Braiding Sweetgrass: Indigenous Wisdom, Scientific Knowledge and the Teachings of Plants*. Milkweed Editions, 2015.

154.) Williamson, Marianne. *Imagine: What America Could Be in the 21st Century: Visions of a Better Future from Leading American Thinkers*. New American Library, 2001.

155.)*Roddick, Anita. Take It Personally: How Globalization Affects You and How to Fight Back. Thorsons, 2001.*

I walk this path. There is no wrath in my pursuit to nurture what this culture lacks. I talk with acts. The pact I have with Mother Earth enacts goodness to extract intellectual gold that corporations, greed, and machines could never exploit, hold, or mine. My goals are woven with divine omens. I am owning my wrongs. Refusing to condone what destroys this land we walk on. The air I breathe relies on trees that are falling to the sins of man. I have a plan to cease the atrocities committed by this human clan. We need change, and I am the man who will unify the guiding forces required to withstand misguided hands that suffocate what this ecosystem depends on to ascend. Aho.

Made in the USA
Columbia, SC
02 October 2021